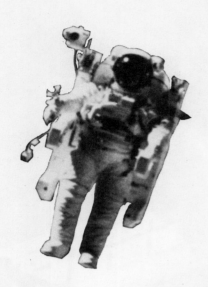

MOMENTS IN SPACE

MOMENTS IN SPACE

The Associated Press

GALLERY BOOKS
An Imprint of W.H. Smith Publishers Inc.
112 Madison Avenue
New York City 10016

Copyright © by The Associated Press, 1986.
All rights reserved.
ISBN: 0-8317-6086-9

Project Director: Dan Perkes
Editor: Norm Goldstein
Photo Editor: Carol Deegan

AP Photo Library (Joan Kearney, director)

Text: John Barbour and Howard Benedict

Design: Robert Pigeon, Combined Books
        and Lizbeth Hoefer-Nauta

Prepared and Produced by
Wieser & Wieser, Inc.,
118 East 25th Street
New York, New York, 10016

Published by Gallery Books, an imprint of
W.H. Smith Publishers, Inc.
112 Madison Avenue
New York, New York 10016

CONTENTS

Preface 7

Early Days 11

Program Mercury 33

Program Gemini 63

Program Apollo 73

Discovery and Exploration 105

Space Shuttle Program 143

PREFACE

The last quarter century or more has been only a tick of time in man's fascination with the heavens. He has cursed them, worshiped them, charted them, made glass lenses to see them better.

The rocks of Stonehenge were arranged by the ancients as a kind of astrological observatory 4,000 years ago. Ptolemy charted the skies over Egypt 2,000 years ago and thought the earth was the center of the universe. Then came legions of others —Galileo, Copernicus, Kepler, Newton — all trying to make sense of the stars and the planets, all trying to find where mankind stood in the universe.

How amazed they would be today if they could see it as we do, how dazzled by the close-up views of the planets, how thrilled to hold a piece of the moon in their hands, how awed by our better measure of the universe, a universe that still exceeds our grasp.

The distances were incredible to contemplate. Shakespeare said of the heavens that it was like man standing on a mountain looking to a far-off shore and wishing his foot were equal to his eye. The puniness of man becomes even more puny as his experience increases. A Soviet cosmonaut walking in space looked back at his spacecraft and said it looked like a lonely planet in a shoreless sea.

The ancient astronomers would be pleased to know that the immensity still awes us. We realize, as they did, that the more we know, the more there is to know; the farther we see, the more distant the limits, if there are any, to the universe.

True, we have photographed our neighboring planets at close range, and stripped them of some of their mystery. We have found Mercury, the closest to the sun, a pocked, airless place, almost solid rock, the surface looking something like a prune.

We found that Venus, our nearest neighbor, is wrapped in carbon dioxide with sulfuric acid clouds, trapping its 900-degree heat and obscuring the surface which has huge circular depressions not seen anywhere else, and a valley 950 miles long, 125 feet wide and three miles deep.

We have seen the rings of Saturn. We thought there were six. There are thousands. We found five new moons around Saturn, making a total of seventeen.

We saw that Jupiter has at least fifteen moons, and a ghostly ring.

We saw Mars in all its diversity, its soil rich in rust, its sparse atmosphere erupting in monstrous dust storms, sweeping the massive volcanoes and dry channels that may have been carved by water ages past. There are no signs of life and temperatures so low that water can exist only as vapor or ice.

In January, 1986, Voyager 2 ended its close-up exploration of Uranus and headed for Neptune for an expected fly-by within 6,000 miles of its moon Triton in 1989.

Then it will join Voyager 1 and the earlier Pioneer 12, traveling outbound to measure the flow of solar particles to determine where the sun's influence ends and where that of other stars begin.

Closer to earth, we have walked the moon, adding footprints to its dusty surface, and we have looked back at earth in all its blue and white majesty. And in between we have begun a regular spaceline, peppering the sky with communications satellites and scores of others to aid navigation, weather reporting, earth observation and dozens of other chores.

Along the way we have seen bravery and superhuman effort. We have seen life and death. We have seen close decisions in orbit around the earth. We have seen a new frontier opening up, a new ocean to sail into, a new challenge to face.

Now we are promised permanent space stations, and new products fashioned in space to serve man on earth. It is only the beginning.

But what a beginning.

This is the photo album of less than three decades of unwavering effort. What a shame Ptolemy, Galileo, Copernicus, Newton and Kepler cannot be here to see it with us. We are the fortunate generation.

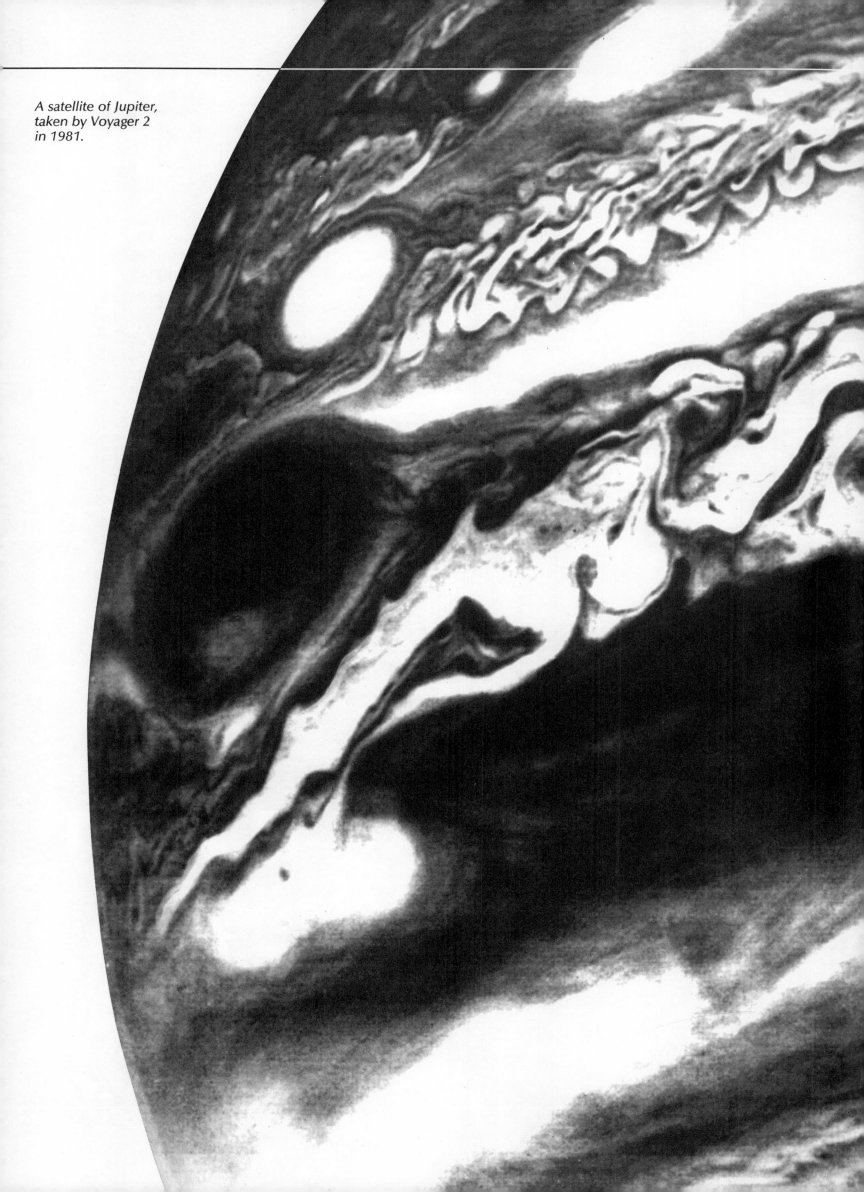

A satellite of Jupiter,
taken by Voyager 2
in 1981.

EARLY DAYS

Man's dreams of space and exploring it have always been a dance between fact and fiction. And why not?

The moon, for instance. What man did not know about the moon, he made up. She lives in a thousand primitive legends and religions. To the Greeks, she was Selene. To the Romans, Diana, twin sister of Apollo. The ancients read everything into the moon. She was made the home of crises, dreams and tranquility. They said she summoned forth were-wolves, was the runaway sister of a sorceress, produced crimes of passion.

The poets had their say. She was Shelley's "orbed maiden," Shakespeare's "inconstant moon," Emerson's "tinsel" in the sky. The poet Francis Thompson had it best. "The innocent moon which nothing does but shine," he wrote, "moves all the laboring surges of the world."

And so the tides obey her. She is written into the calendar in days and months. Her passage keeps time with the metabolism of mice and fiddler crabs. So many things tick to the lunar clock. She brings the rock crab ashore to feed, makes the grunion run, times the cycle of human fertility.

So should it be any wonder that a child of the 20th century, Robert Goddard, should dream of flying into space. Fiction preceded his dream. He devoured Jules Verne's tale of a journey to the moon. Likewise H.G. Wells' "The War of the Worlds." But Goddard was not a writer. He was a scientist, an inventor, intent on making fact out of fiction.

He read everything he could find about rocketry, from the primitive rockets of the early Chinese to the English rockets that lit up the sky over Fort McHenry, so that Francis Scott Key could tell through the night that our flag was still there.

Inset: *Dr. Robert H. Goddard, "the father of rocketry," in 1935.*

The lunar horizon, as seen during the Apollo 8 lunar orbit mission in 1968.

Dr. Robert H. Goddard.

But Goddard was thinking of the moon. In 1919, at the age of 37, he wrote a booklet entitled "A Method of Reaching Extreme Altitudes." It laid out his calculations and formulas for mass, thrust, velocity, distance. Goddard spent a lifetime with his meager funds, testing liquid against solid fuels, lightweight metals, pressures and rocket plumbing. On March 16, 1926, in a field in Auburn, Massachusets, he erected his rocket. Fueled from separate tanks by gasoline and liquid oxygen, his ten-foot rocket struggled off his primitive launching pad, finally built up speed to over sixty miles an hour and reached a height of 184 feet before veering off to one side and falling back to earth.

Dr. Robert H. Goddard with his liquid-propellant rocket Auburn, Massachusetts, in 192

Dr. Robert H. Goddard.

He was ridiculed most of his life for trying to make his dreams come true, and he did not live long enough to see men rocket into space. Today he is recognized as the "father of rocketry," and his name graces the Goddard Space Flight Center. He once wrote H.G. Wells, "There can be no thought of finishing. For aiming at the stars . . . is a problem to occupy generations . . . There is always the thrill of beginning."

On the eve of Apollo 11, his widow remembered an entry in his diary, "When old dreams die, new ones come to take their place. God pity a one-dream man."

Goddard was not alone. In the Soviet Union, Konstantin Tsiolkovsky, and in Germany, Hermann Oberth, worked on rocketry. The V-2 rocket of World War II that razed much of London was an example of German expertise, and after the war it was V-2 technology that became the basis of America's early rockets.

German scientists of the V-2 experimental laboratory at Pennemunde (left to right): Major General Walter Dornberger, Lieutenant Colonel Berbert Aster, Wernher von Braun (with sling), Hans Lindberg, after surrender to U.S. 7th Army troops in 1945.

Sequence shows a remade German V-2 rocket fired in a test at White Sands Proving Grounds, New Mexico.

A captured German V-2 rocket is fired from the deck of the USS Midway in 1947.

But the United States was only toying with space rockets. Its main postwar purpose was developing rocketry as armament.

Russians look skyward from the astronomical grounds of the Moscow planetarium, searching for Sputnik I.

Then, on October 4, 1957, the Soviet Union cracked the fragile shell that embraces mankind on earth. It orbited a 184-pound sphere. Sputnik I shocked the world. The United States, which thought of itself as the world's leader in technology, began to reassess everything from its national aims to its educational system.

An Atlanta, Georgia, restaurant offered a "Sputnikburger," complete with "small dog" and garnished with Russian dressing.

A replica of Sputnik I hangs in the Moscow Exhibition Hall.

(Left to right) *Major General J.B. Medaris, Army Ballistic Missile Agency commander; Army Chief of Staff General Maxwell D. Taylor, and Army missile expert Wernher von Braun with what was called a prototype of a scientific satellite.*

At Huntsville, Alabama, that overcast, warm autumn day, a team of German rocket scientists and engineers, the same group that designed the V-2 which lambasted London, were hosting the new Secretary of Defense, Neil McElroy. There was a cocktail party and dinner the night before at a restored 100-year-old farmhouse named, appropriately, "The Goddard House."

It was the Army's chance to persuade McElroy that the German scientists could beat the Soviets into space with an upgraded V-2 design called the Redstone, named after the arsenal where the Germans worked. But a ringing telephone made their proposal academic. They were told that Sputnik I was in orbit.

Major General John Bruce Medaris, who headed the arsenal, recalls the unleashed frustration from Wernher von Braun:

"We knew they were going to do it. Vanguard (the low budget satellite project guided by the Navy) will never make it. We have the hardware on the shelf. For God's sake, turn us loose and let us do something. We can put up a satellite in sixty days, Mr. McElroy. Just give us a green light and sixty days."

Major General J.B. Medaris (left) *and Wernher von Braun with model of Redstone missile.*

Medaris remembers cautioning his chief scientist, "No Wernher. Ninety days."

The year before they had test-fired a modified Redstone, called the Jupiter-C, 3,000 miles out over the Atlantic and 600 miles high. They asked for but were denied permission to use the backup Jupiter-C, designated Missile 29, to put a satellite into orbit. Missile 29 was put in a garage-like shed, in storage.

Dr. Wernher von Braun, when he was technical director at the Army Ballistic Missile Agency, Redstone Arsenal, Huntsville, Alabama, in 1957.

Laika, before space trip in Sputnik II in 1957.

No wonder their frustration now.

But now, the Army experts were certain Sputnik would do what their arguments failed to do. So they wheeled Missile 29 out of the garage, dusted it off and waited.

In vain. The Eisenhower administration, intent on keeping the scientific project separate from the military rocket program, stuck with Project Vanguard.

A month later, the Soviets launched Sputnik II, a 1,000-pound chamber with a live passenger, a dog named Laika, a sacrifice to see if a living creature could endure weightlessness. There was no doubt that a human passenger was in their plans.

Laika in pressurized cabin in Sputnik II 130 miles above the Earth.

Vanguard rising only a few feet before falling over and bursting into flame.

Then, in December, Vanguard appeared ready to hurl its grapefruit-sized satellite into orbit to measure the shape of the earth. World attention focused on Cape Canaveral, Florida.

The countdown reached zero. Orange flame began to billow from the rocket. It rose slightly, and barely two feet over the pad fell back on itself in a huge fireball. Goddard's primitive rocket thirty-one years before had done better.

Vanguard test rocket before firing at Cape Canaveral, Florida, i
December 195.

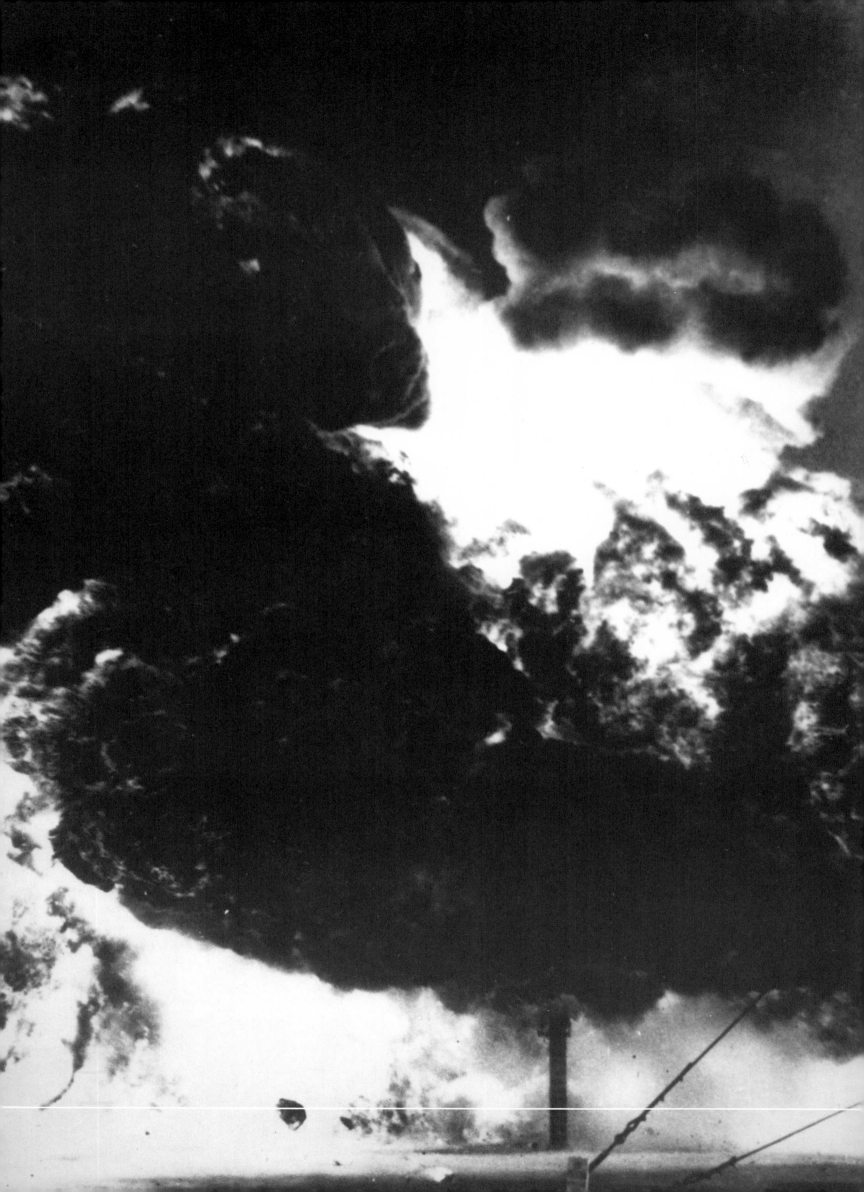

Dr. Wernher von Braun at a Senate Labor and Public Welfare hearing involving science and education matters for national defense, in 1958.

Now U.S. embarrassment was complete. Finally the Army team was given a go-ahead. They shipped their Missile 29 to Cape Canaveral in January for launch later in the month. Von Braun was told he would not be able to see his rocket attempt to reach space. He would have to be in Washington for a news conference after launch.

Vanguard in flames after exploding on launch.

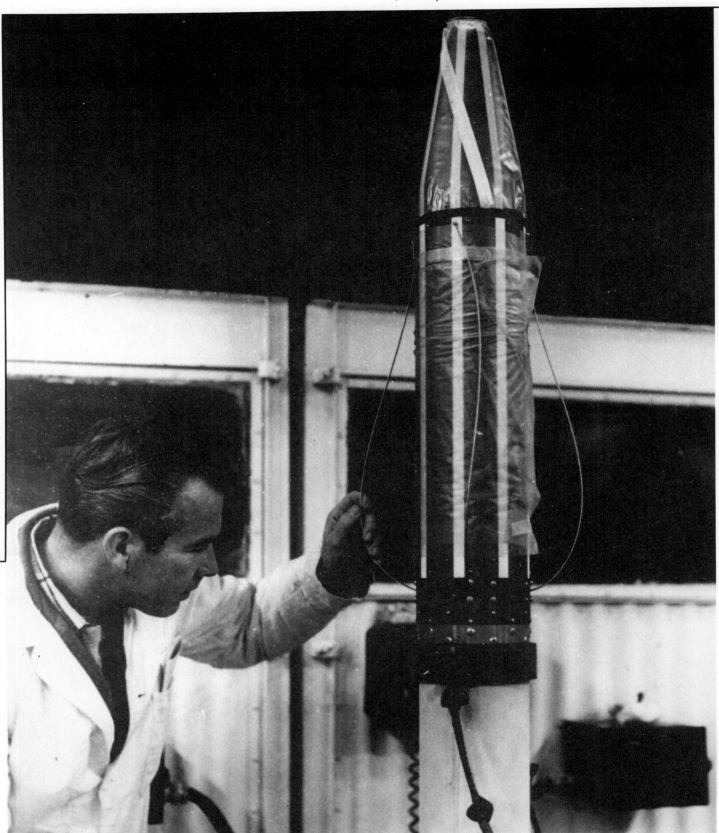

A closeup of Explorer I, weighing 37.1 pounds.

The scientists were poised in their blockhouse on January 28. But that day and the next two they were stymied by the jet stream, a river of wind traveling 200 miles an hour over the Cape. Finally on January 31, 1958, the countdown reached the final twenty seconds. A key was turned and the rest of the firing sequence was automatic.

"Firing command . . . Main stage ignition . . . Liftoff."

Sequence shows Jupiter-C rocket taking off with Explorer I satellite attached.

The white missile rode its tail of fire into the sky. Down-range stations picked up the signals, but the satellite's beeping radio would have to be picked up by the Jet Propulsion Laboratory's big radio dish at Goldstone, California, before orbit could be confirmed. The minutes dragged by. The satellite was late. Finally someone handed General Medaris a slip of paper. It said, "Goldstone has the bird." And then a telephone call from Washington, the Secretary of the Army telling Medaris, "Call it Explorer."

The United States had broken the ice. It succeeded on two out of three Explorers in the following months, and Vanguard finally redeemed itself. In December, 1958, an Atlas rocket was orbited carrying a tape-recorded Christmas message from President Eisenhower, broadcast to the world. But nothing could cover the fact that the United States was late and clumsy getting into space.

A Columbus, Ohio, moonwatch team scans the skies for America's first satellite, Explorer I.

Explorer I satellite is launched January 31, 1958.

A model of the Soviet Vostok spaceship, which took Yuri Gagarin into earth orbit.

PROGRAM MERCURY

The Soviets had bigger rockets. They were first in every department. By 1961, they had launched twice as many pounds into space with less than a third the number of launches.

They had fired two dogs into space orbit and recovered them alive and well. They fired at and hit the moon. They went beyond it and photographed its hidden side. And then a Soviet cosmonaut, Yuri Gagarin, became the first human to orbit the earth.

Soviet space vehicle carries Yuri Gagarin in April 12, 1961, launching.

Photograph of technicians making final tests on the spaceship of Soviet cosmonaut Yuri Gagarin is from a Soviet documentary film, "First Voyage to the Stars."

Soviet Major Yuri Gagarin, first man to orbit the earth.

ove: NASA's Project Mercury astronauts in 1959 (left to right): Alan B. Shepard, M. Scott Carpenter, John H. Glenn, Donald K. Slayton, Virgil Grissom, Walter M. Schirra, and (bottom) L. Gordon Cooper.

In space suits, the Project Mercury astronauts, left to right, front row, Walter Schirra, Donald Slayton, John Glenn, and M. Scott Carpenter; back row, Alan Shepard, Virgil Grissom, and L. Gordon Cooper.

Life Magazine featured the original Project Mercury astronauts on its cover in 1959. From left, top: Walter M. Schirra, Alan Shepard Jr.; center, John H. Glenn, M. Scott Carpenter and Donald K. Slayton; bottom, L. Gordon Cooper Jr. and Virgil Grissom.

Wives of the seven Mercury astronauts in 1961. Left to right, first row, Mrs. M. Scott Carpenter, and Mrs. Donald Slayton; second row, Mrs. L. Gordon Cooper, Mrs. Walter Schirra and Mrs. Alan Shepard; third row, Mrs. Virgil Grissom and Mrs. John Glenn.

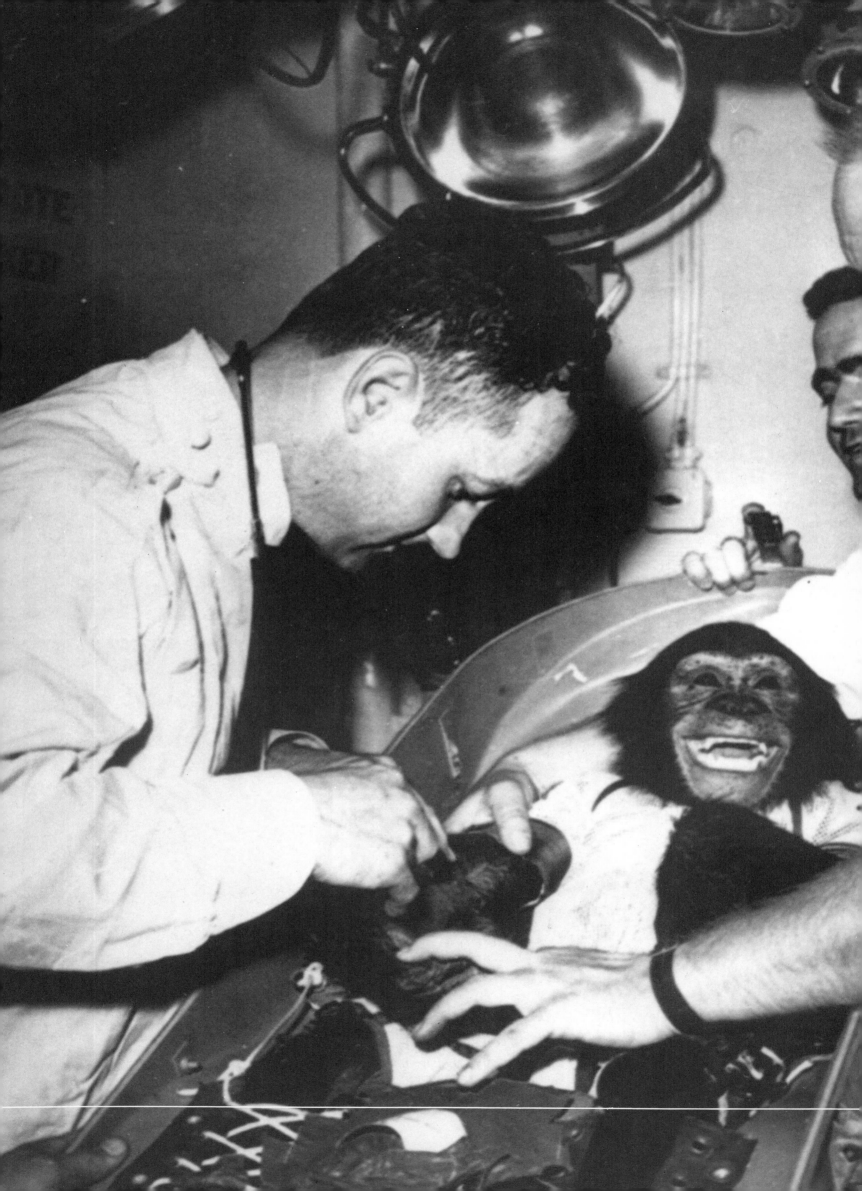

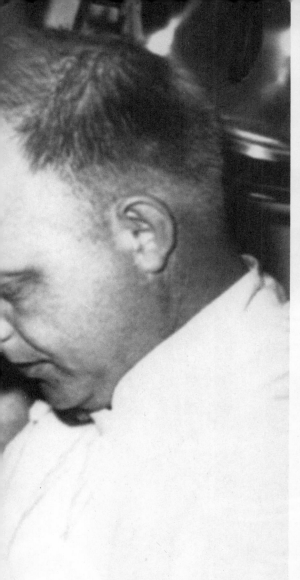

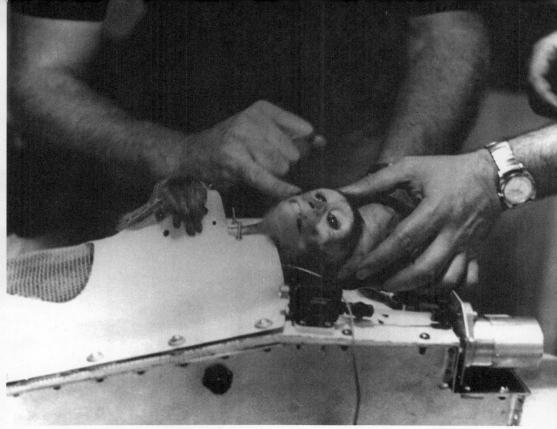

Monkey Able is released from life support capsule after riding a Jupiter missile into space with another monkey, Baker, in 1959.

Ham is examined by Air Force Major Richard Benson after the chimp's ride 420 miles down the Atlantic missile range in a Mercury-Redstone rocket.

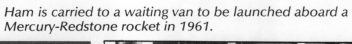

Ham is carried to a waiting van to be launched aboard a Mercury-Redstone rocket in 1961.

Ham, the first chimpanzee to ride into space, after his return from a flight aboard a Redstone rocket in 1961.

Then, less than a month after Gagarin's epic flight, America tasted its first meaningful success. Navy Commander Alan Shepard Jr. blasted off from Cape Canaveral on a sixteen-minute flight 116 miles high and landed safely 302 miles downrange in the Atlantic.

The nation listened as from one radio, watched as from one television set.

SHEPARD: Ahh, Roger; lift off and the clock is started.
. . . Yes sir, reading you loud and clear. This is
Freedom 7. The fuel is go . . . oxygen is go . . .
Freedom 7 is still go. . . . What a beautiful sight. . . .

Astronaut Alan B. Shepard Jr., in Freedom 7 capsule before launch on a 15-minute suborbital flight in 1961.

Alan Shepard is hauled aboard the recovery ship in the Atlantic after his flight.

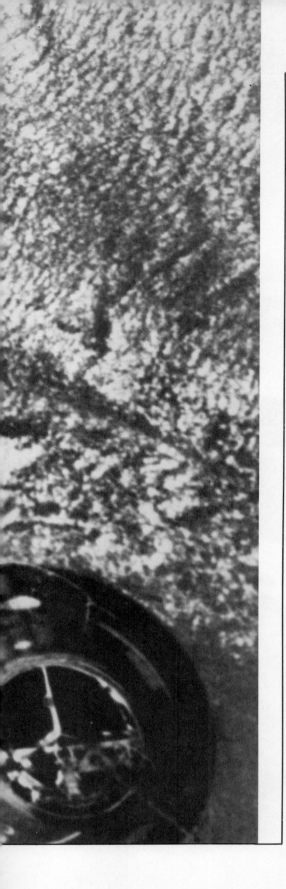

He was looking at the white-edged, green headlands of the Eastern seaboard strung out behind him. As thrilling as it was to the nation however, it was a very small step after Gagarin's flight. It did show that the nation believed and it had a hero finally.

The United States was still playing catchup, but its space program found a larger focus, a greater commitment. Twenty days after Shepard's flight, the president addressed Congress on urgent national needs. He included space.

KENNEDY: I believe this nation should commit itself to achieving the goal, before the decade is out, of landing a man on the moon and returning him safely to earth. No single project in this period will be more impressive to mankind, or more important for the long-range exploration of space; and none will be so difficult or expensive to accomplish.

With that he put the pride and the resources of the nation behind a goal that rose above the space race, beyond the Russians, to that ghostly companion in the sky that has haunted the human mind forever.

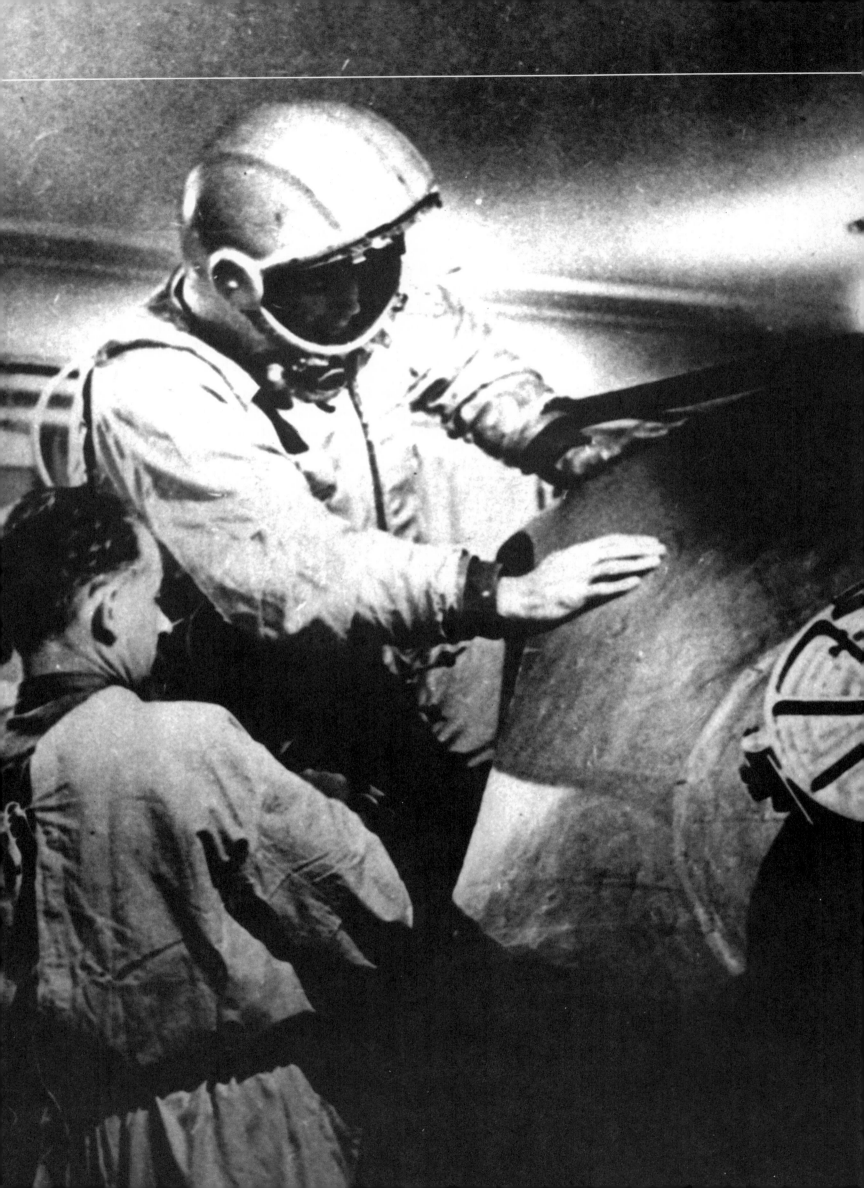

Soviet cosmonaut Gherman Titov prepares for a training flight in 1961.

After Gus Grissom repeated Shepard's flight, the space agency was ready to orbit, matching Gagarin. But the Russians had already leapfrogged Gagarin.

Less than three weeks after Grissom's flight, they launched Gherman Titov on a safe and successful seventeen orbits of the earth.

Cosmonaut Gherman Titov in centrifuge during training for orbital flight he made in August 1961.

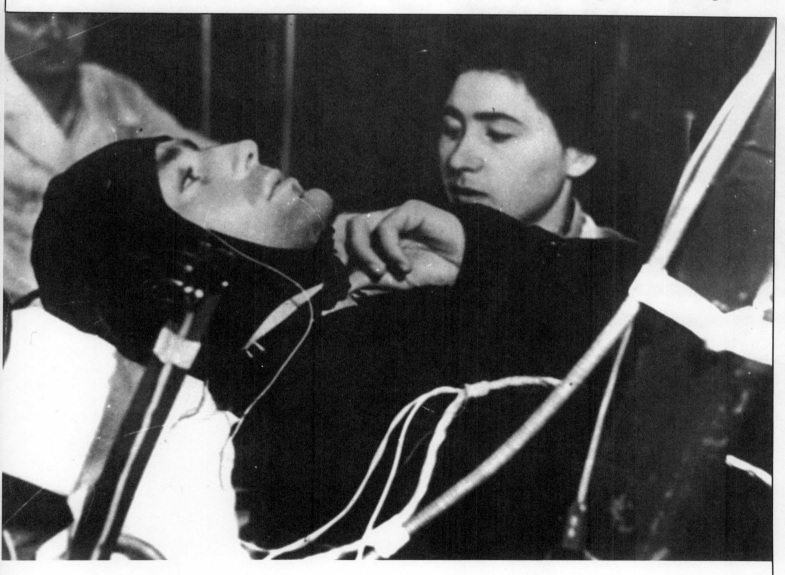

John Glenn climbs into Friendship 7 capsule at Cape Canaveral,
Florida, February 20, 1962.

Astronaut John Glenn rides in transfer van from Hanger S to launch pad at Cape Canaveral.

John Glenn, chosen for the first American orbital flight, seemed in every sense the All-American hero. Freckled, boyish, a crack pilot who shot down three MiGs in Korea, was decorated 23 times, a religious man who married his childhood sweetheart, a family man who sent tapes home to his children so they could hear his voice, feel his absence less.

The nation was getting lessons in rocketry, in orbital flight, slighty more than half a century after the Wright brothers flew their flimsy craft at Kitty Hawk. The focus now was an Atlas rocket, built to carry a nuclear warhead. Instead it would carry a man.

John Glenn on his way back after three orbits of the Earth on February 20, 1962.

John Glenn is shown at about the time he re-entered the earth's atmosphere and described the capsule as a "fireball."

Finally on the morning of February 20, 1962, after many postponements, everything came together — weather, machine and man. Slowly, with a sound that shook the air for miles around, the 125-ton rocket pushed the 168-pound man toward space. Around the country, telephone calls dropped to nearly nil as the nation watched and listened.

There was wonder in Glenn's voice as he hurtled through his mere three orbits. The world heard, if it could not see.

> GLENN: Zero Gs and I feel fine. . . . Capsule is turning around. Oh, the view is tremendous. . . . I can see the booster doing turnabouts just a couple of hundred yards behind. It looks beautiful. The horizon is a brilliant blue. There I have the mainland in sight . . . and have the Canaries in sight through the window . . .

He saw the lights of Perth, Australia, turned on in his honor. He could not hear the New York subway conductor telling his passengers by loudspeaker than John Glenn was in orbit — "please say a little prayer for him."

Coping with a balky maneuvering thruster, Glenn had to override the automatic system and fly Friendship 7 himself, proof of the value of a man at the helm.

John Glenn shows his three reflection mirrors as he prepares for orbital flight.

Capsule with astronaut John Glenn bobs in Atlantic Ocean after his historic three-orbit flight.

Friendship 7 capsule with John Glenn aboard is pulled on to destroyer Noa after recovery in Atlantic.

There were motorcades for him from Cocoa Beach, Florida, and nearby Cape Canaveral to the tickertape of New York City. President Kennedy, speaking in the Rose Garden, gave thanks:

"We have a long way to go in this space race. We started late. But this is a new ocean, and I believe the United States must sail on it and be in a position second to none. Some months ago I said that I hoped every American would serve his country. Today Colonel Glenn served his."

The man who set the goal of the moon would not live to see it won. But he had set things in motion. There was much more to be done.

John Glenn at New York tickertape parade.

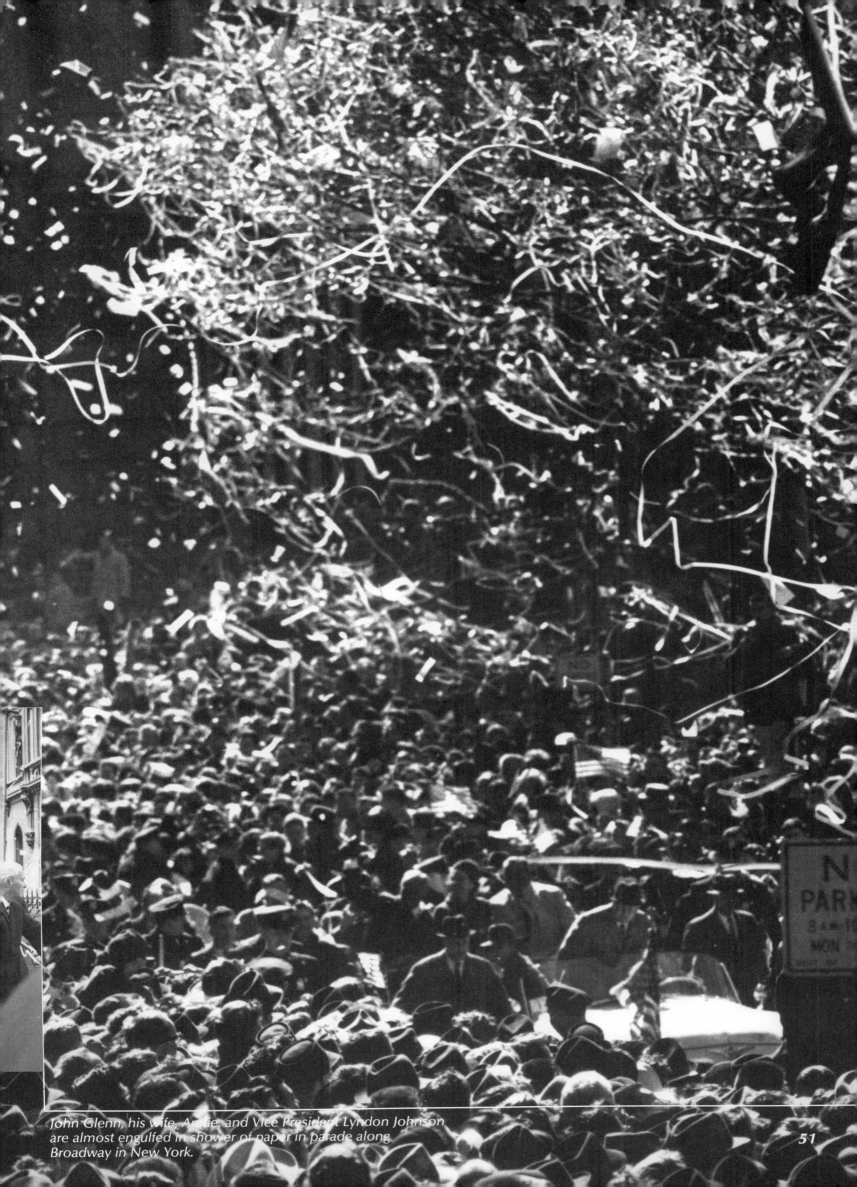

John Glenn, his wife, Annie, and Vice President Lyndon Johnson are almost engulfed in shower of paper in parade along Broadway in New York.

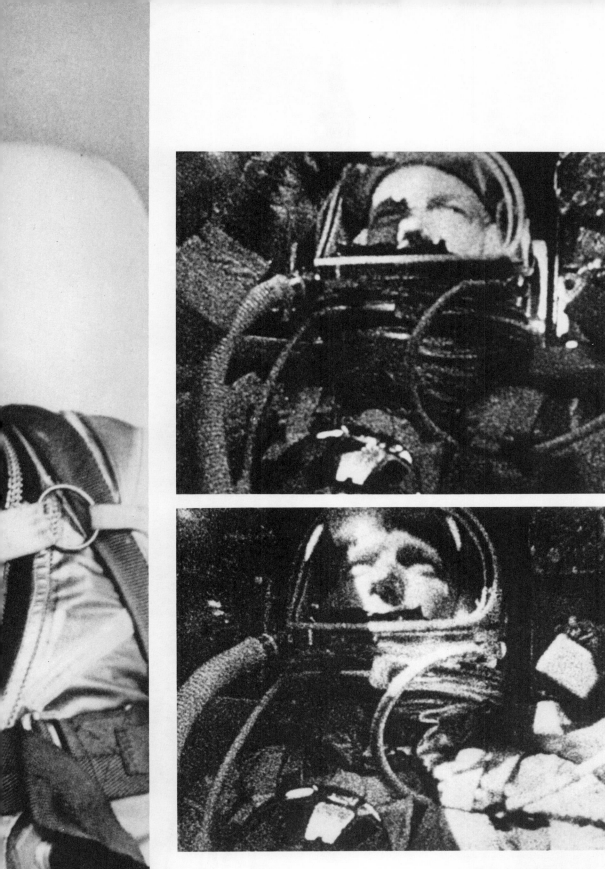

An automatic camera recorded astronaut M. Scott Carpenter in his Aurora 7 capsule in space, May 24, 1962.

There was a seeming barrage of Mercury flights —Scott Carpenter repeating Glenn, Wally Schirra six orbits, Gordon Cooper twenty-two orbits, two years after Shepard.

Astronaut M. Scott Carpenter, reflecting mirror on his chest, prepares for 1962 launch in Aurora 7 capsule.

Astronaut
L. Gordon Cooper
parachutes into
the Pacific aboard
Faith 7 capsule.

Dripping seawater, Sigma 7 spacecraft with astronaut Walter Schirra aboard is
lifted to the deck of carrier Kearsarge after six-orbit flight in 1962.

Atlas rocket blasts off,
lifting astronaut
L. Gordon Cooper into
orbit in 1963.

Spaceship Faith 7, with astronaut L. Gordon Cooper aboard, is lifted on to the carrier Kearsarge after recovery near Midway Island in the Pacific.

Faith 7 capsule is readied for L. Gordon Cooper's flight from Cape Canaveral, Florida.

French newspapers headline L. Gordon Cooper's 22-orbit flight.

Astronaut L. Gordon Cooper blasts off from Cape Canaveral May 15, 1963.

Six of the seven Mercury astronauts at NASA's manned space research laboratory in Houston, Texas, in 1962. Left to right: Donald K. Slayton, L. Gordon Cooper, Alan B. Shepard, Project Mercury Director Robert R. Gilruth, M. Scott Carpenter, Walter Schirra, Virgil Grissom.

A Navy helicopter hauls astronaut M. Scott Carpenter from the sea in a sling after his three-orbit flight. His Aurora 7 spacecraft bobs in the water, at lower left.

MANNED SPACECRAFT CENTER
IAL AERONAUTICS AND SPACE ADMINISTRATION
HEADQUARTERS

Astronaut M. Scott Carpenter and his wife Rene are welcomed
with a Cocoa Beach, Florida, parade after his orbital flight.

Crowds in New York's Grand Central Terminal watch huge
screen televising M. Scott Carpenter's flight.

Cosmonaut Valentina Tereshkova, the first woman in space.

The Russians were now orbiting two spacecraft together in parallel flight paths. In one was the first woman in space, Valentina Tereshkova, who would later marry another cosmonaut.

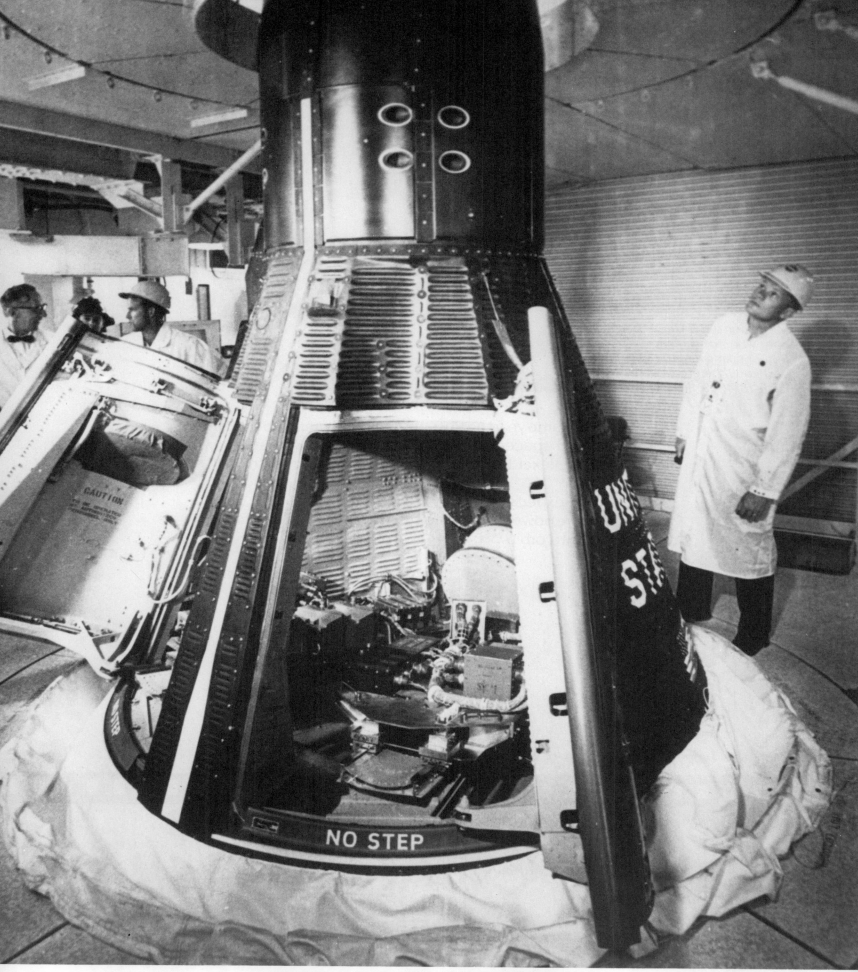

PROGRAM GEMINI

The United States was moving slowly, it seemed, but deliberately. In 1964 they tested an unmanned maneuverable Gemini two-man ship and a dummy three-man Apollo, the vehicle that would eventually be aimed at the moon.

Above: Astronaut Neil Armstrong (right) inspects Gemini capsule, while astronaut L. Gordon Cooper (with hard hat, rear left) talks with engineers.

Cosmonaut Alexei Leonov boards gantry elevator taking him to Voshkod II before its March 18, 1965, flight.

      The same year the Russians put three men into orbit in a Voshkod spacecraft, and six months later in another Voshkod, Alexei Leonov became the first human to walk in space.

      U.S. experts estimated that Soviet rockets were three times more powerful than the Titan booster that would send Gemini into orbit.

Cosmonaut Alexei Leonov leaves spaceship for walk in space.

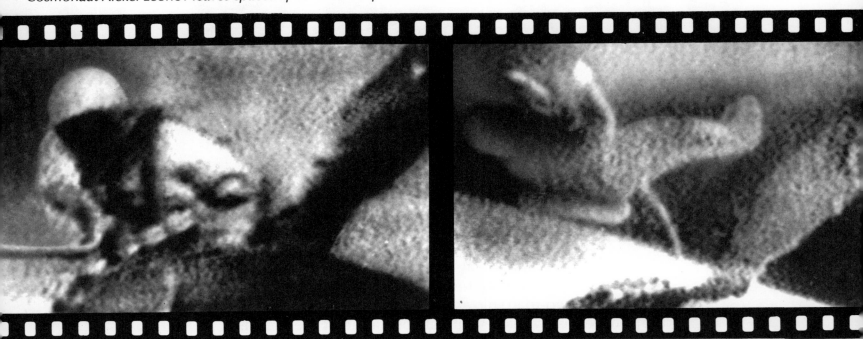

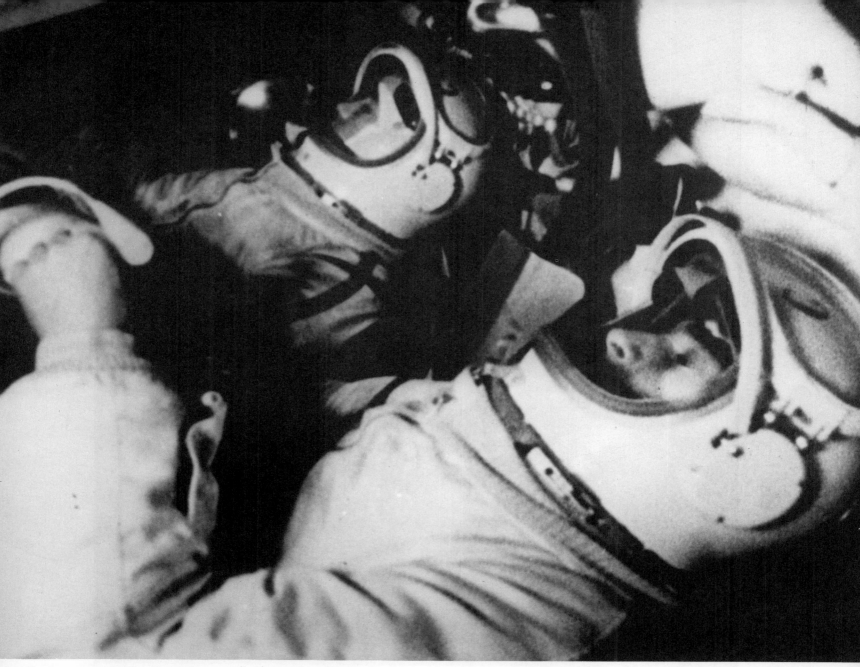

Soviet cosmonauts Alexei Leonov (left) and Pavel Belyayev await blastoff of Voskhod II at Baikonur in the Soviet Union, March 18, 1965.

Cosmonaut Alexei Leonov climbs out of Voskhod II hatch to float in space, free of his capsule.

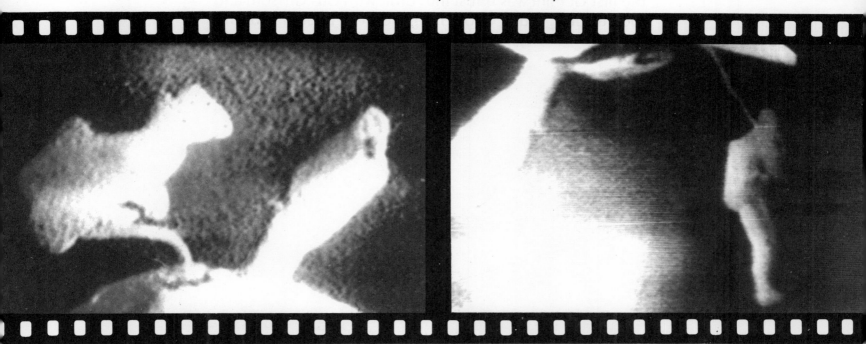

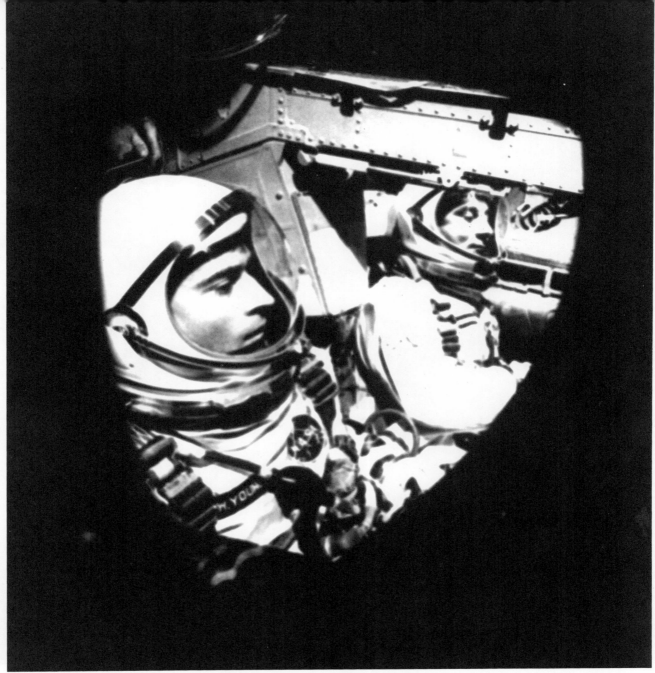

Astronauts John W. Young (front) and Virgil Grissom in their Gemini spacecraft before 1965 flight.

Less than a week after Leonov's space walk in 1965, the first Gemini was thrust into orbit with Gus Grissom and rookie John Young aboard. In the next twenty months, Gemini would fly twenty men into space.

Gemini was the training ship for Apollo, testing man-euverability in space, bringing back pictures of how one spacecraft looked to another, joining up with an orbiting engine, and letting astronaut Edward Higgins White II walk, tethered, in space, like a man walking a dog.

Astronaut Ed White walked in space for twenty minutes in 1965.
Fellow astronaut James McDivitt took the picture from the
Gemini 4 capsule.

Astronaut Ed White is photographed by James McDivitt from the Gemini 4 capsule as White made America's first space walk, maneuvering with the aid of an oxygen rocket gun.

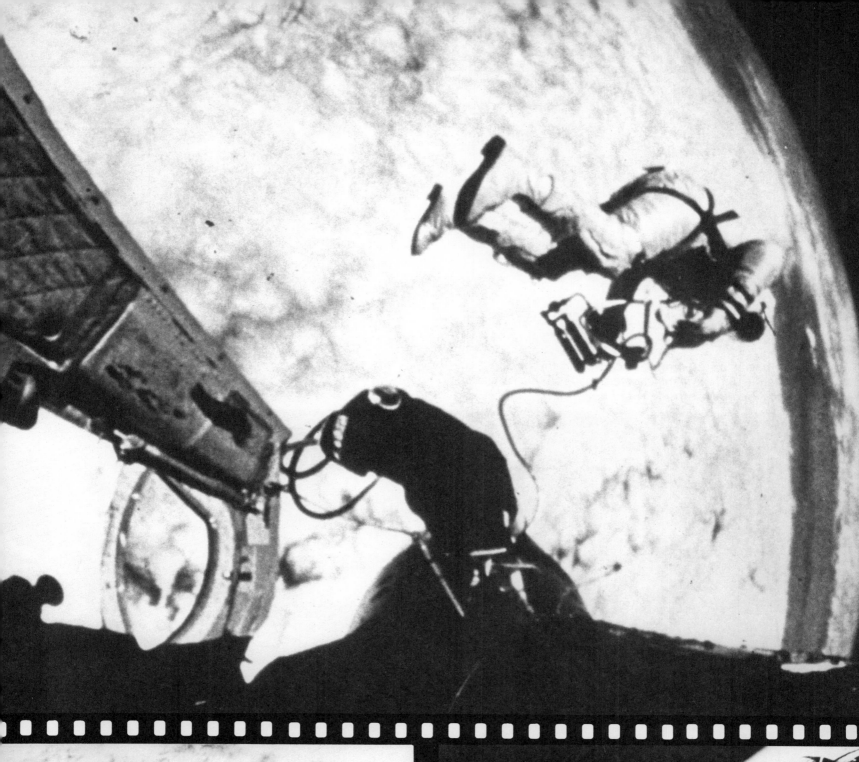

69

Ed White begins his 20-minute excursion in the trackless void of space, a tether and oxygen lifeline emerging from a black bag that left the Gemini 4 capsule with him.

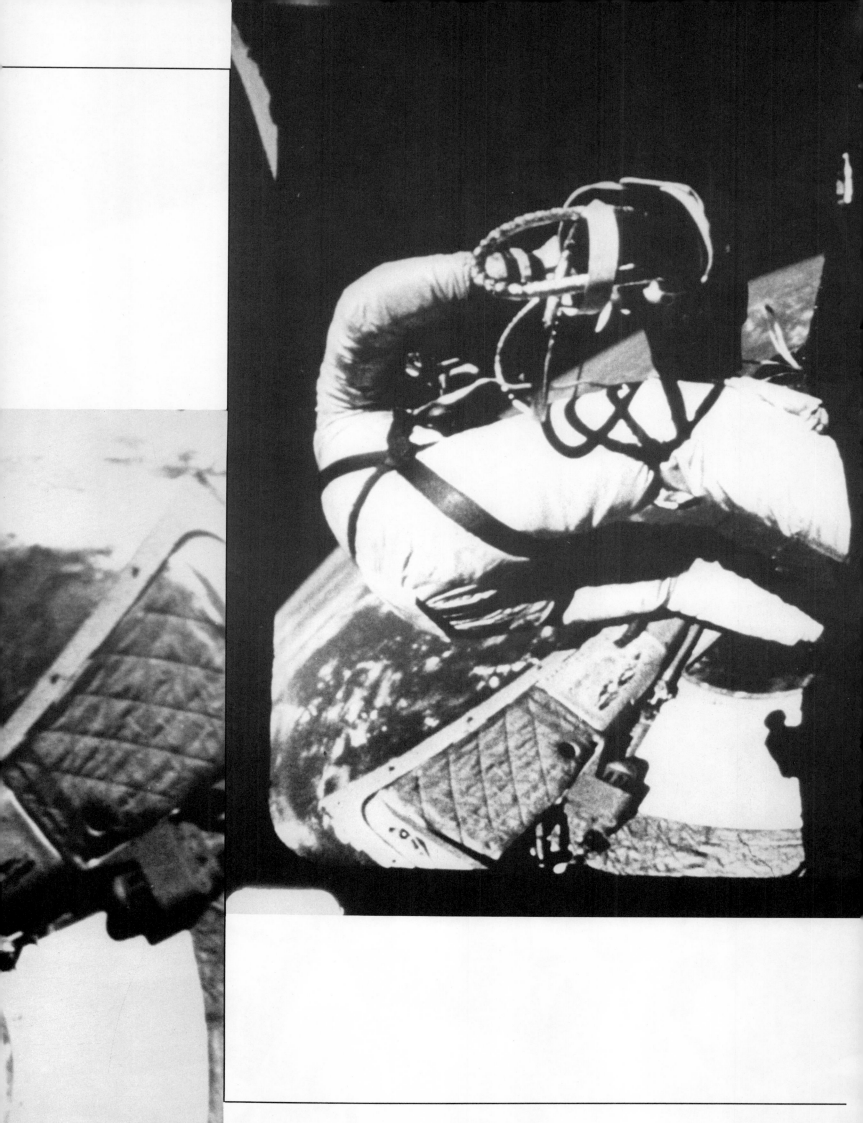

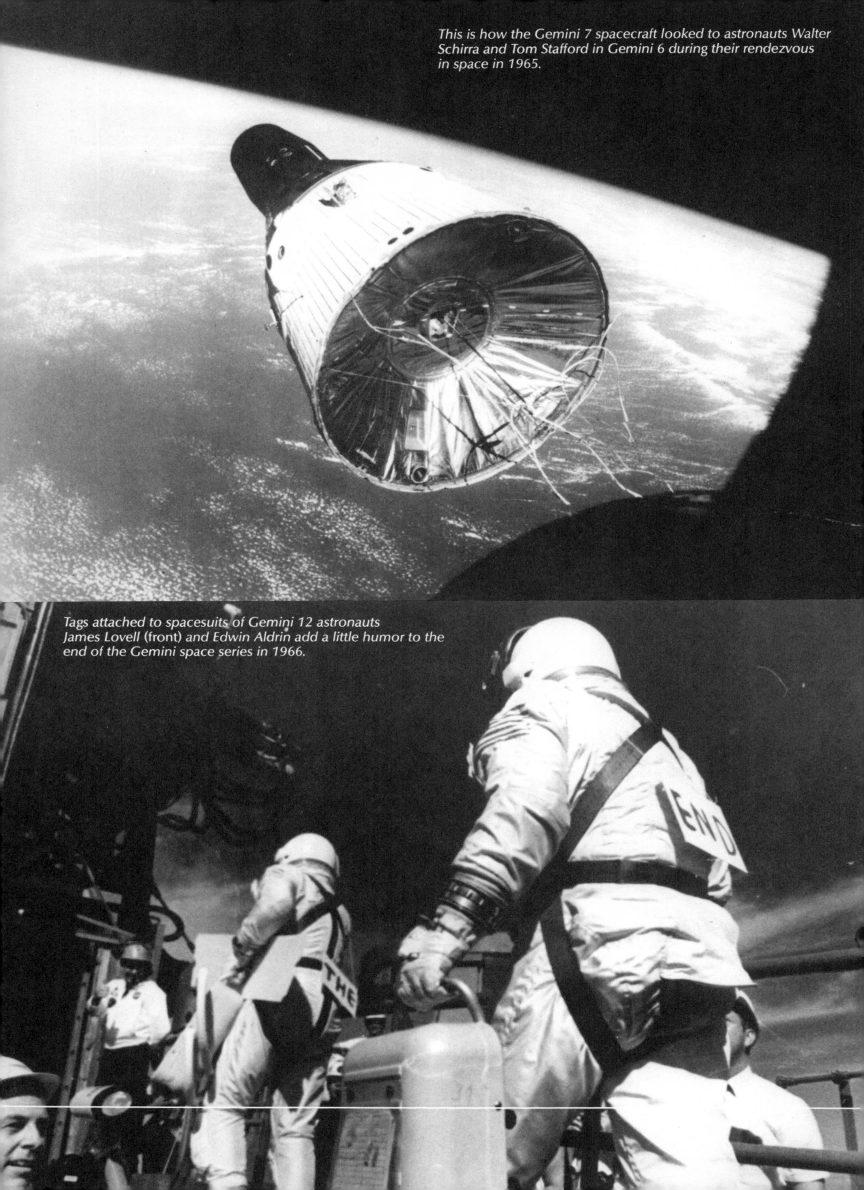

This is how the Gemini 7 spacecraft looked to astronauts Walter Schirra and Tom Stafford in Gemini 6 during their rendezvous in space in 1965.

Tags attached to spacesuits of Gemini 12 astronauts James Lovell (front) and Edwin Aldrin add a little humor to the end of the Gemini space series in 1966.

PROGRAM APOLLO

When Gemini ended, Apollo was not yet ready. Far from it. It nagged Grissom who was slated to lead the first trio testing Apollo that some 20,000 test failures had been noted in Apollo development, but he kept it private.

An artist's drawing shows the Lunar Orbiter spacecraft reaching the moon.

The charred interior of the Apollo I spacecraft after the fire that killed Ed White, Roger Chaffee and Virgil Grissom.

On January 27, 1967, he, Ed White and Roger Chaffee suited up for a countdown rehearsal in the cabin pressurized with 100 percent oxygen. As the countdown ticked down, they reported bad smells in the cabin and encountered communications problems, wondering aloud how they would radio back from the moon if they couldn't reach Mission Control a few miles away.

Then there was a babble of voices. Chaffee shouted, "We've got a fire in the spacecraft." Abetted by the pure oxygen, the fire never gave them a chance — Grissom, Chaffee and White were the first to die in the space race.

Three months later, the Soviets launched a new spacecraft called Soyuz, which means union, and was meant for rendezvous and docking. The pilot was Colonel Vladimir Komarov. After twenty-seven hours in space, flight bulletins ceased. The landing parachutes failed. Komarov was dead.

Both space programs were now in trouble, but the Americans rallied.

Charred area of Apollo I spacecraft, near the floor of the left hand equipment bay, after fire killed three astronauts in 1967.

Sign at a Cocoa Beach, Florida, restaurant spells out the feelings of residents who were proud to have the astronauts in their midst.

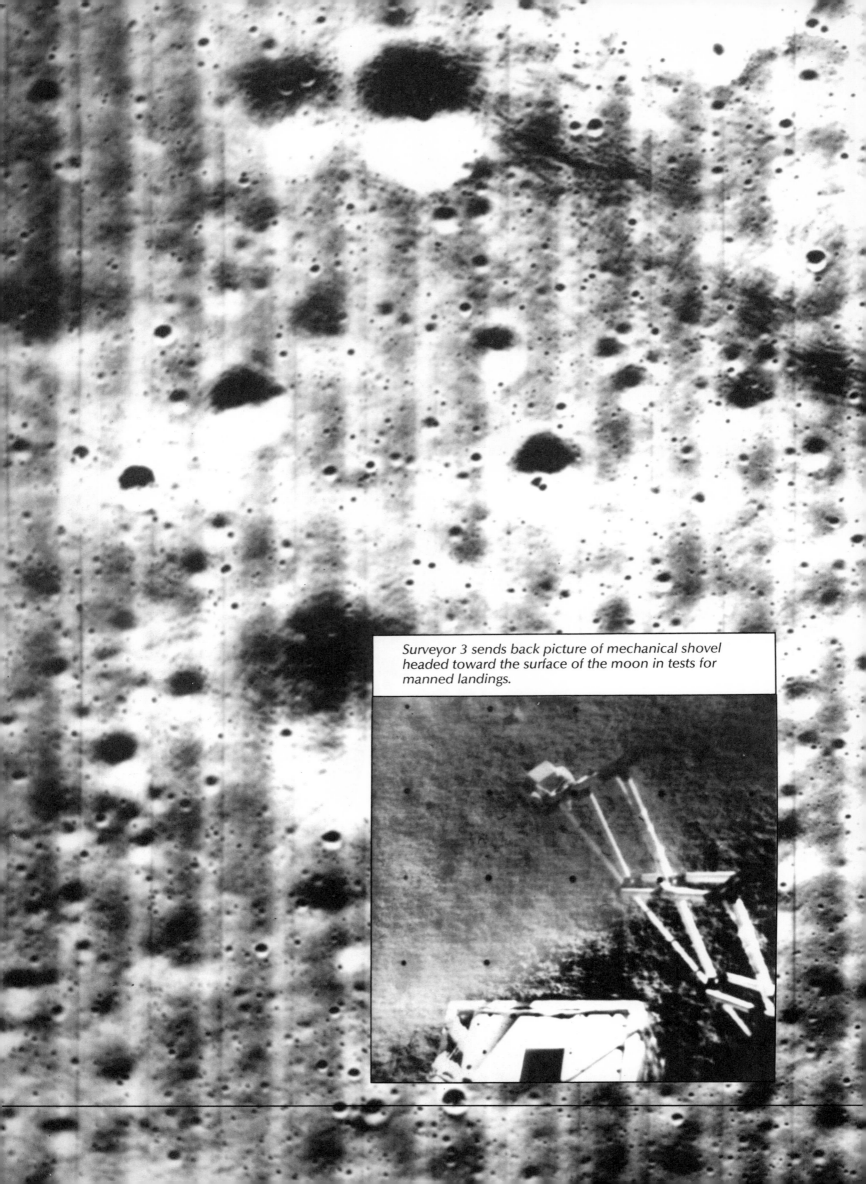

Surveyor 3 sends back picture of mechanical shovel headed toward the surface of the moon in tests for manned landings.

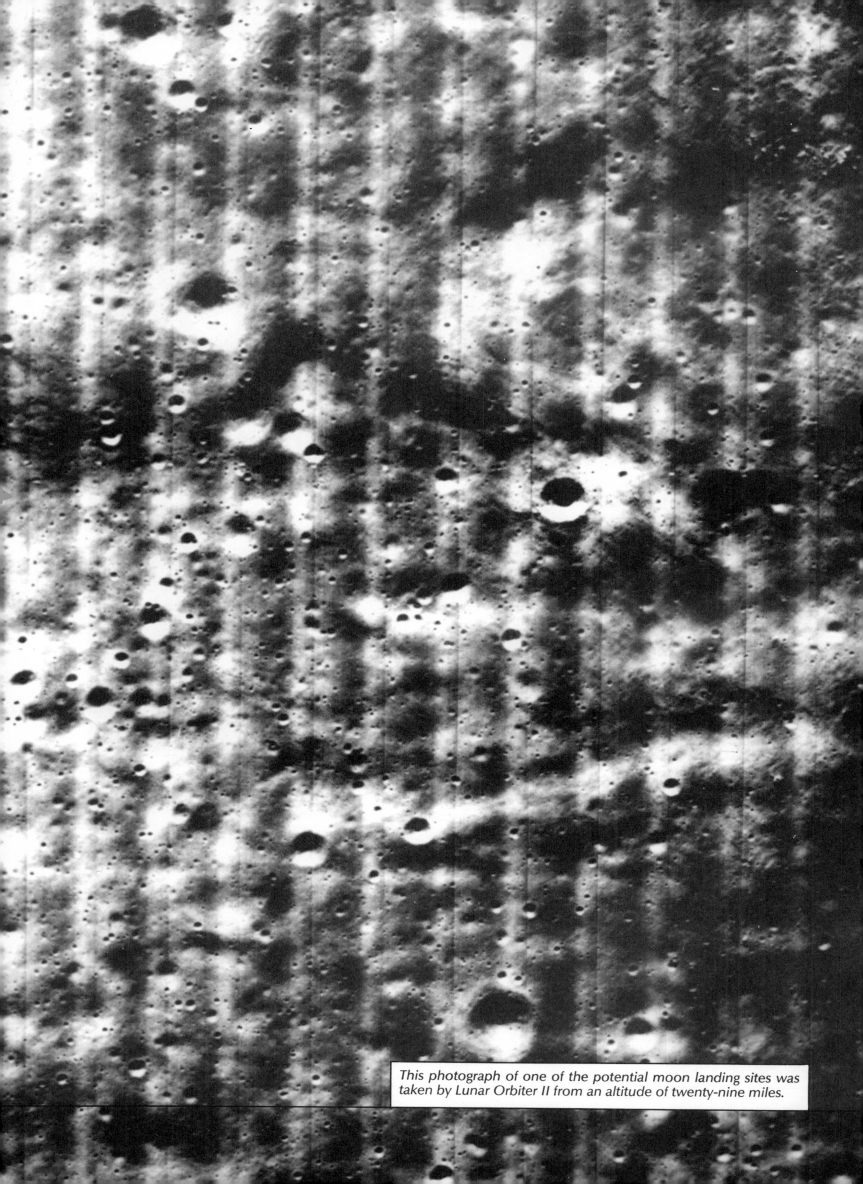

This photograph of one of the potential moon landing sites was taken by Lunar Orbiter II from an altitude of twenty-nine miles.

Astronaut Donn Eisele on Apollo 7, holds sign announcing
start of telecast from the space flight: "From the Lovely Apollo
Room High Atop Everything."

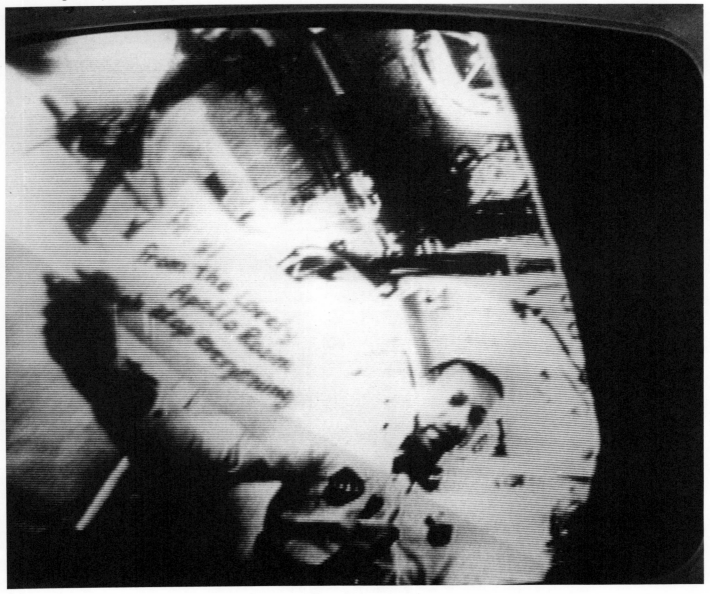

In November 1967 they tested the Saturn 5 rocket and
late in 1968 a three-man crew flew Apollo 7 into earth orbit
and brought it back.

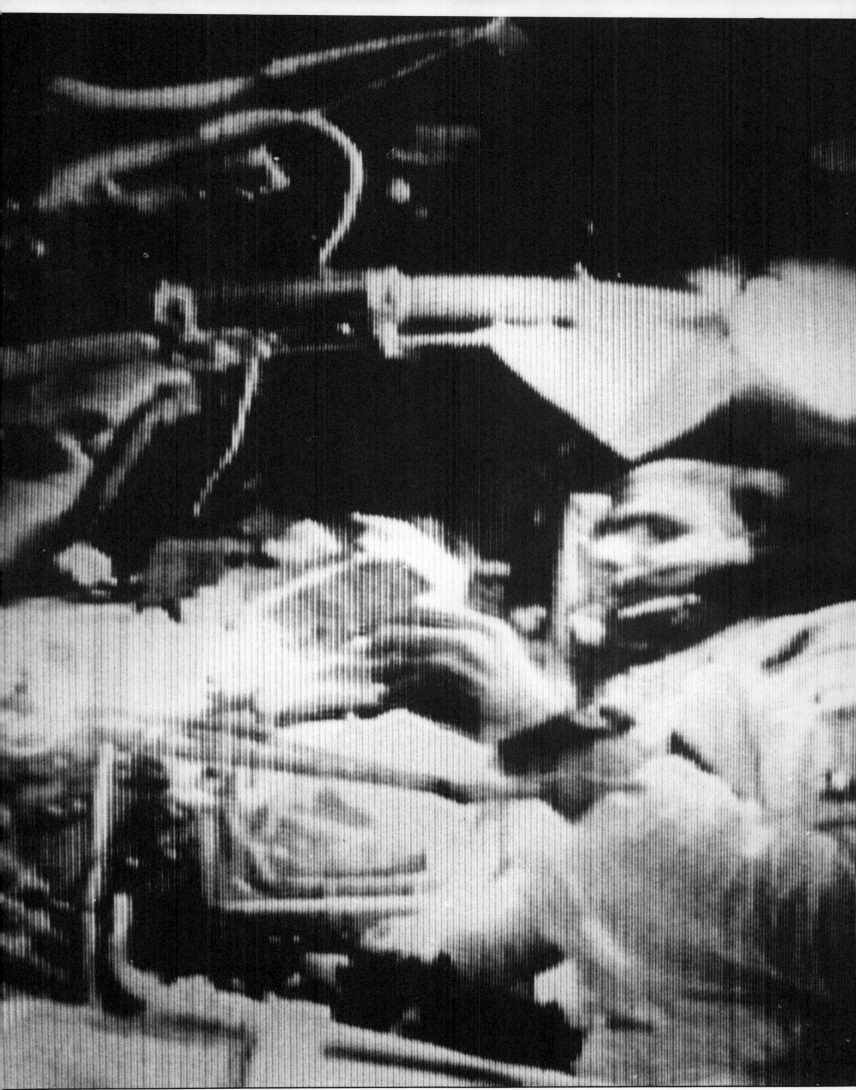

William A. Anders, lunar module pilot of Apollo 8, prepares
Christmas dinner for the crew during 1968 flight.

The rising Earth greeted Apollo 8 astronauts as they came from behind the moon in Christmas 1968 flight.

From Apollo 11, Earth rising above the moon's horizon.

They decided to get a closer view of the moon with Apollo 8, which would fly without the lunar lander, which was not yet ready.

A few days before Christmas, Frank Borman, Jim Lovell and Bill Anders, atop the giant Saturn 5, waited.

CONTROL: Sixty seconds and counting as we come up on a flight to the moon. Ignition, we have ignition.

The Saturn 5 performed beautifully. It put Apollo 8 into earth orbit, from which they fired the third stage engine again to head for the moon, and for the first time they could see the earth becoming smaller and smaller.

Both sides of the Atlantic Ocean are visible in this view from Apollo 8. The most prominent land mass is the bulge of West Africa.

Africa is at the center of the photo of Earth from Apollo 11.

Earth, from Apollo 8 near the moon.

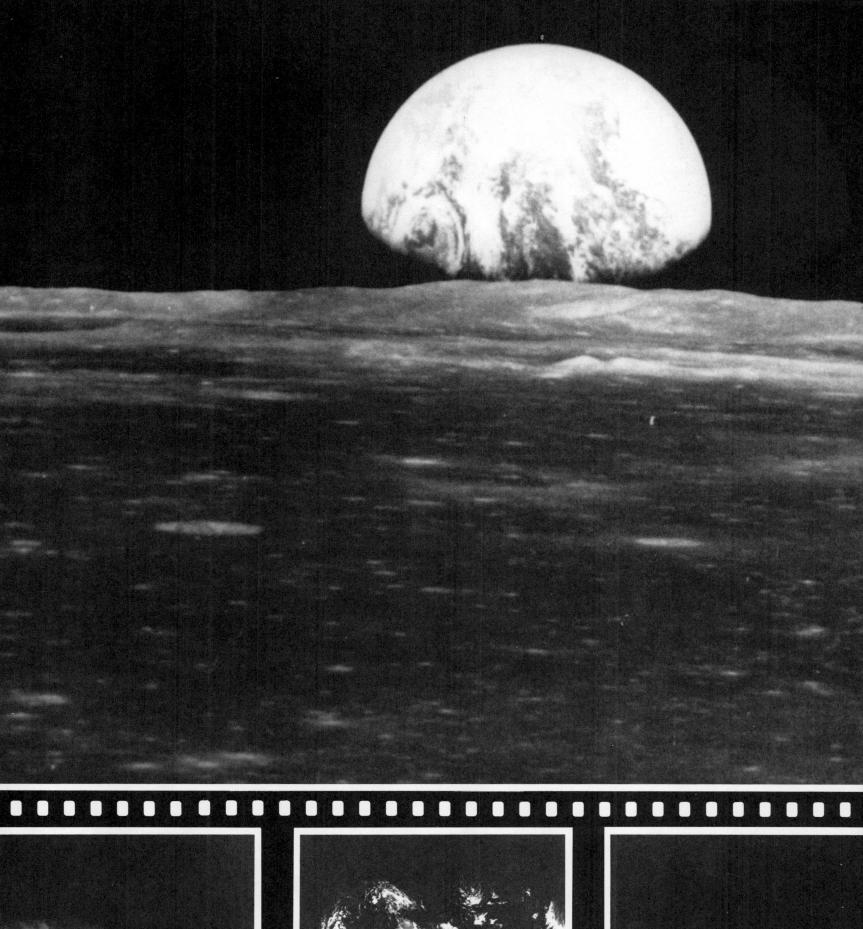

The moon, looking toward the Sea of Tranquility.

The astronauts described vividly the whitish gray surface of the moon, like dirty beach sand with lots of footprints in it, as Anders reported and the world saw from television cameras. But the crew had something special planned for this Christmas season. Borman had said before he left that he hoped the flight would prove this was really one world, and why can't we learn to live together like decent people?

Photo from Apollo 8 looks at the large crater Goclenius.

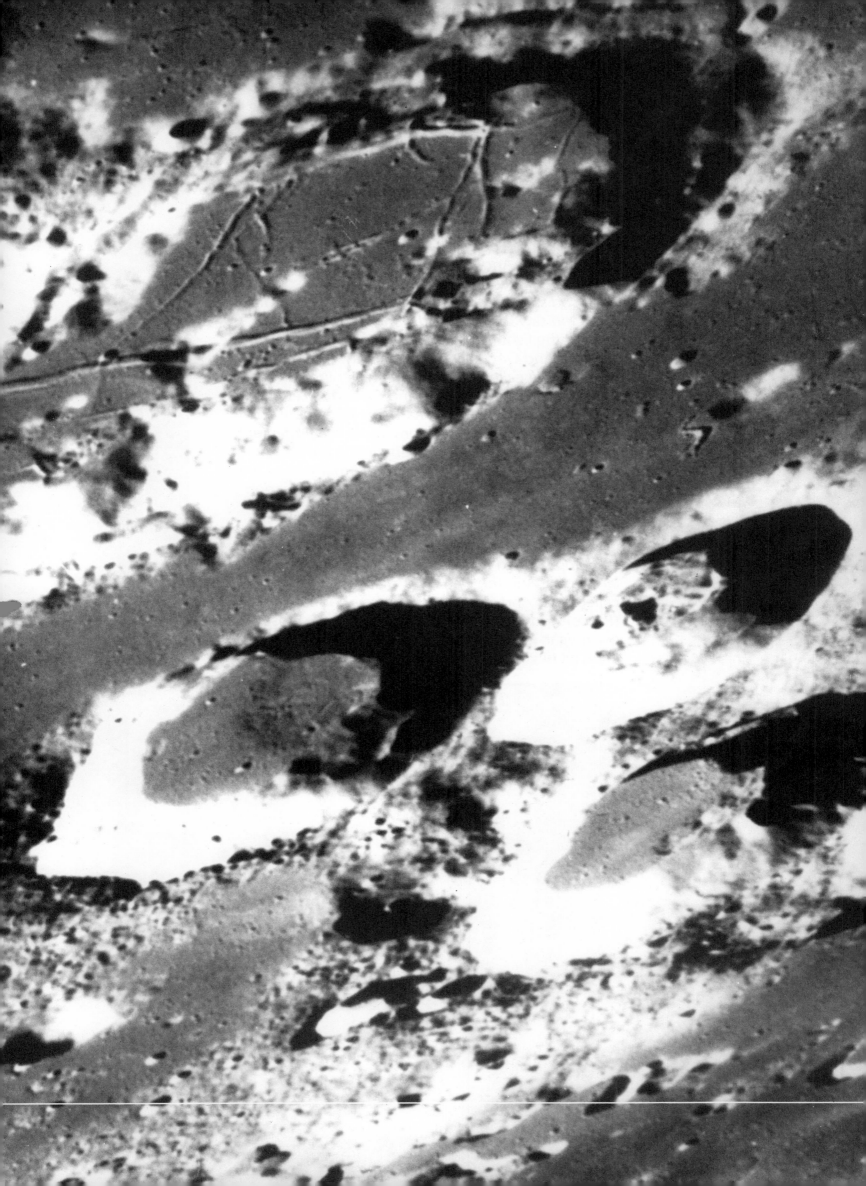

With the earth dressed up for Christmas 240,000 or so miles away, the Apollo 8 crew trained their cameras on the lunar desert which recalled a lifeless earth. Anders began reading, followed by Lovell and Borman:

ANDERS: In the beginning, God created the heaven and the earth. And the earth was without form, and void and darkness was upon the face of the deep. And God said, Let there be light. And there was light. And God saw the light, and it was good. And God divided the light from the darkness.
LOVELL: And God called the light day. And the darkness He called night. And the evening and the morning were the first day. And God said, Let there be a firmament, and God made the firmament and divided the waters which were under the firmament from the waters which were above the firmament. And it was so. And God called the firmament heaven. And the evening and the morning were the second day.
BORMAN: And God said, Let the waters under the heavens be gathered in one place. And let the dry land appear. and it was so. And God called the dry land earth. And the gathering together of the water He called seas. And God saw that it was good.
(Pause) And from the crew of Apollo 8, we close with goodnight, good luck, a Merry Christmas, and God bless all of you, all of you on the good earth.

An oblique view of the lunar horizon, taken during the Apollo 8 mission.

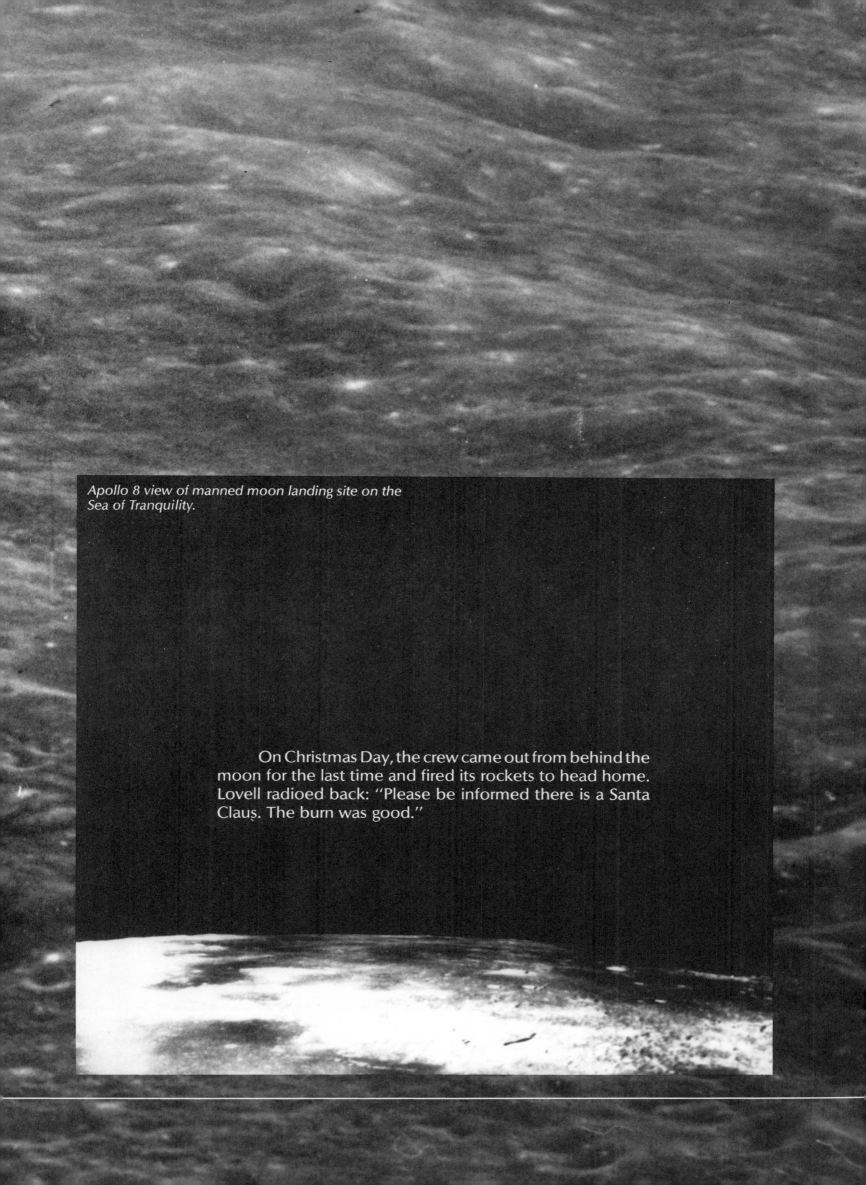

*Apollo 8 view of manned moon landing site on the
Sea of Tranquility.*

On Christmas Day, the crew came out from behind the
moon for the last time and fired its rockets to head home.
Lovell radioed back: "Please be informed there is a Santa
Claus. The burn was good."

This Apollo 12 photograph shows two U.S. spacecraft on the moon. The Apollo 12 lunar module is in the background, behind Surveyor 3.

Apollos 9 and 10 tested out the lunar lander and the techniques of joining it up with the mother ship Apollo again. The stage was now set for the finale.

A composite picture of the moon, with circle marking the projected landing site of Apollo 11.

More than a million people flocked to the Cape to see Apollo 11 blast off. The world sat on the edge of its chair. The isolation van was ready to accept the Apollo 11 crew — Neil Armstrong, Edwin "Buzz" Aldrin and Mike Collins — lest they pick up some strange germ from the lunar surface that would spread over the earth.

They would go into earth orbit, then fire again toward the moon, then Armstrong and Aldrin would board the little lunar lander Eagle for the trip to the moon's surface, set up their experiments and fly Eagle back to the mother ship which Collins had patiently flown in, waiting. The radio voices were full of encouragement.

CONTROL: It is a beautiful morning for a trip to the moon . . . Good luck and Godspeed from the launch crew . . .
ARMSTRONG: Thank you very much, we know it will be a good flight.

And a good flight it was. Like clockwork, the Saturn 5 ignited, and gulping fifteen tons of fuel a second, shot them on their way. The next burn took them out of earth orbit and their color television cameras showed the retreating earth.

On their thirteenth orbit of the moon, 100 hours away from earth, Armstrong and Aldrin disengaged Eagle from the mother ship and turned toward our moon. With them they carried tokens of the space race dead — Grissom, White, Chaffee, Komarov and Gagarin who had died in a plane crash.

The little Eagle sought out the landing spot on the rocky, dusty Sea of Tranquility, nudging down ever so slowly against the power of its landing rocket, dodging boulders and rocks. Dust kicked up all over from the surface. An edgy landing.

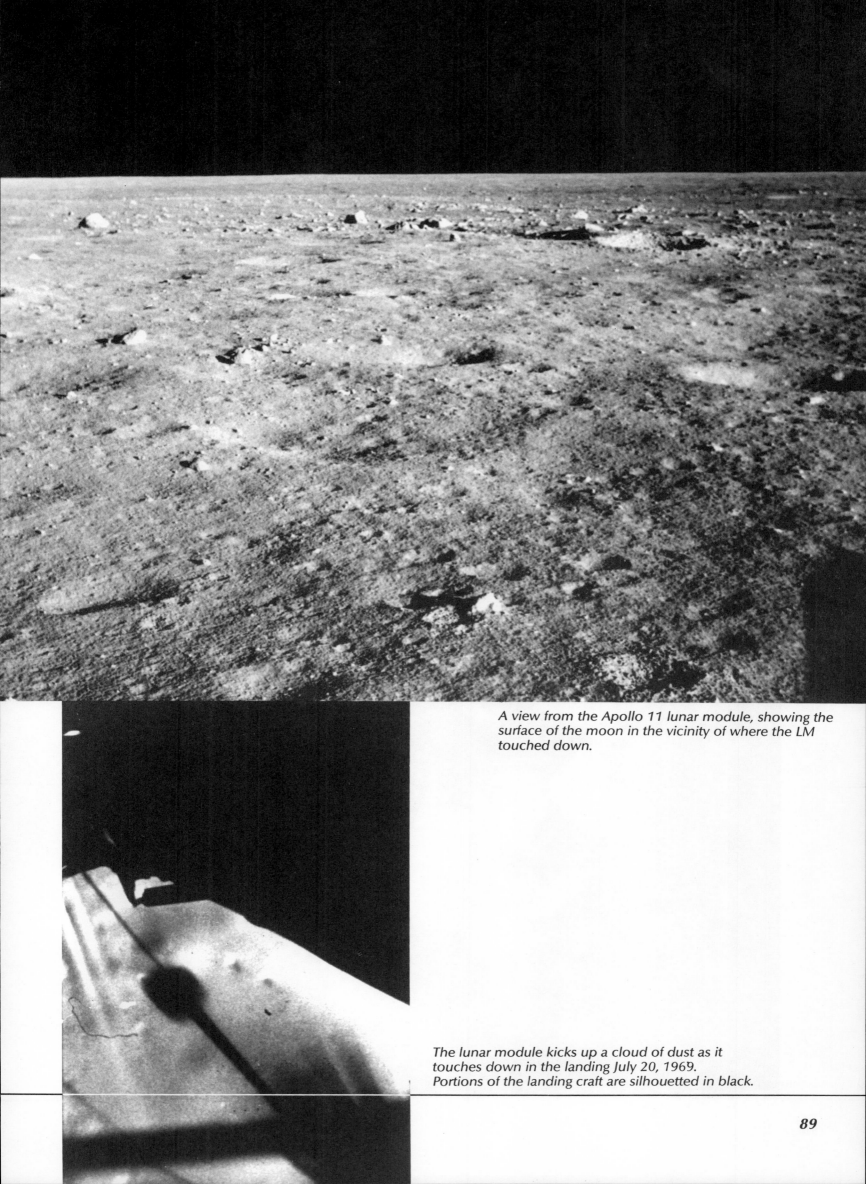

A view from the Apollo 11 lunar module, showing the surface of the moon in the vicinity of where the LM touched down.

The lunar module kicks up a cloud of dust as it touches down in the landing July 20, 1969. Portions of the landing craft are silhouetted in black.

And then it was still.

ARMSTRONG: Houston . . . Tranquility Base here. The Eagle has landed.
CONTROL: Roger Tranquility. We copy you on the ground. You got a bunch of guys about to turn blue. We're breathing again.

It was 4:18 p.m. Eastern Daylight Time, Sunday, July 20, 1969. Some 240,000 miles away, the earth seemed to wear an excited grin, at least a relieved smile.

Apollo 11 astronaut Neil Armstrong steps down from the lunar module ladder to become the first man on the moon.

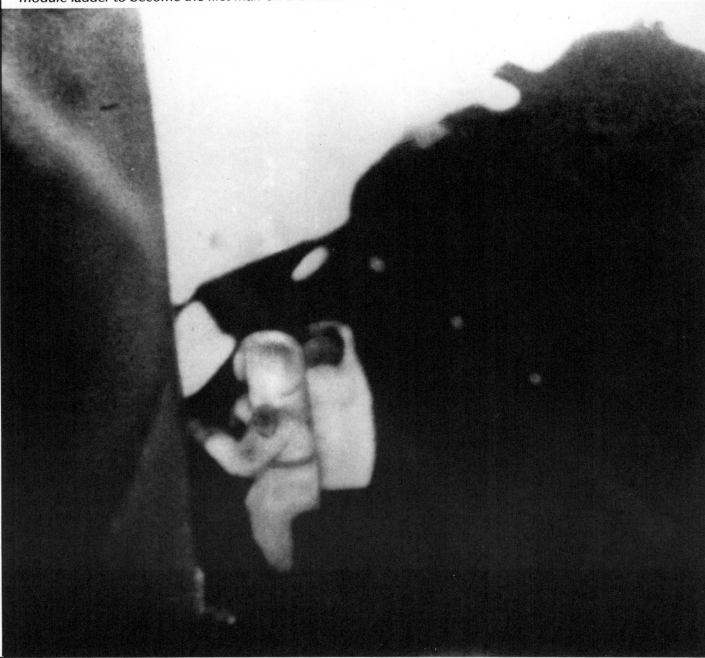

NASA photo shows astronaut footprint on the moon.

A little more than six hours later, after setting things in order inside Eagle, and fetching the American flag they would plant on the lunar surface in their two-and-a-half-hour lunar walk, they emerged and climbed to the surface, Armstrong first, Aldrin twenty minutes later.

When Armstrong's 9½-sized boot touched the surface he took one awkward step backwards from the ladder. His voice crackled hesitatingly, "That's one small step for a man, one giant leap for mankind."

The race that was not a race was won. But President Kennedy's dedication of the U.S. space program still rung true. He had said, "Now is . . . the time for a great new American enterprise — time for this nation to take a clearly leading role in space achievement which in many ways may hold the key to our future on earth."

Inset: *Astronaut Neil Armstrong, the U.S. flag, the lunar module, and television camera are reflected in the face mask of astronaut Edwin Aldrin on the moon.*

Footprints of astronauts Neil Armstrong and Edwin Aldrin in the lunar soil. Part of the lunar module is silhouetted in the background.

Astronaut Edwin Aldrin walks on the moon.

Astronauts Gene Cernan (right) and Harrison Schmitt after they unturled the U.S. flag on the moon on Apollo 17's 1972 flight.

Apollo 11 astronauts Neil Armstrong and Edwin Aldrin plant the U.S. flag on the moon after man's first landing on the lunar surface in 1969.

Neil Armstrong and Edwin Aldrin on the moon.

Astronaut Edwin Aldrin examines the U.S. flag on the moon. Fellow astronaut Neil Armstrong took the picture.

Edwin Aldrin carries two pieces of the Early Apollo Scientific Experiments Package across the surface of the moon.

With the lunar module in the background, Edwin Aldrin sets up a seismic experiment on the moon.

Neil Armstrong photographed moon companion Edwin Aldrin setting up an experiments package during the Apollo 11 EVA.

The Soviet Soyuz spacecraft photographed from a rendezvous window of the U.S. Apollo spacecraft.

When the Soviet Union lost the moon race to the United States it concentrated on developing a series of small space stations named Salyut to study the long-term effects of space weightlessness on space travelers. Cosmonauts shuttled back and forth to these stations, with some groups staying in orbit for more than 200 days at a time. The Soviets said they need this information for building more permanent stations and for one day dispatching a manned expedition to Mars. A spaceship would take seven months to reach Mars and another seven months to return to earth. A highlight of the 1970s was a joint mission in which spaceships of the Soviet Union and United States linked up in orbit. The two nations are considering the possibility of again joining together for the Martian expedition.

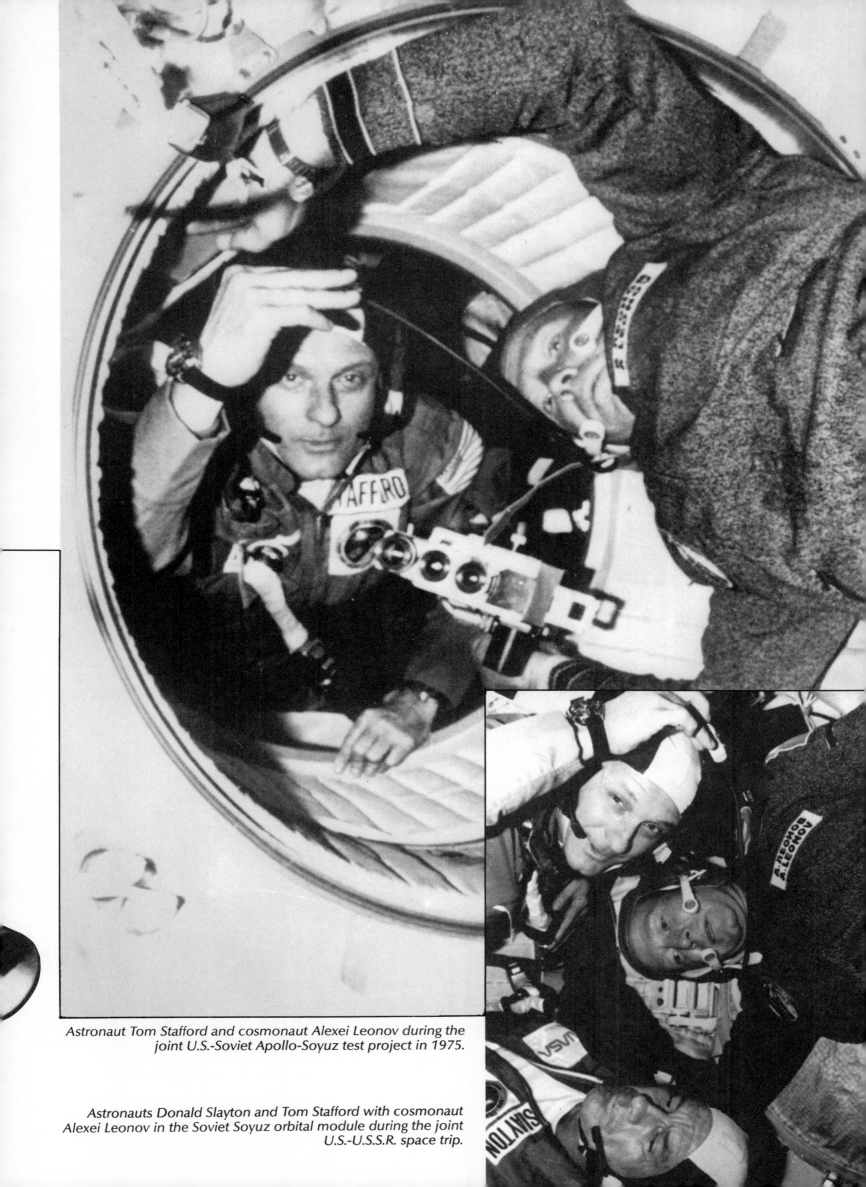

Astronaut Tom Stafford and cosmonaut Alexei Leonov during the joint U.S.-Soviet Apollo-Soyuz test project in 1975.

Astronauts Donald Slayton and Tom Stafford with cosmonaut Alexei Leonov in the Soviet Soyuz orbital module during the joint U.S.-U.S.S.R. space trip.

Apollo 17 astronauts Gene Cernan (left) and Harrison Schmitt walk across the lunar landscape in 1972.

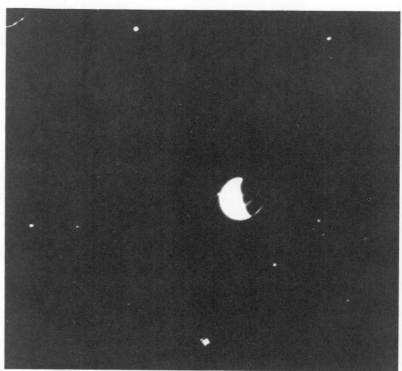

The Earth is photographed in far-ultraviolet light by astronaut John W. Young during the Apollo 16 mission in 1972.

A group of moon rocks is in the foreground, with the mountains of the Hadley Apennine group in the background, in this Apollo 15 photo.

Six teams of Americans — a total of twelve astronauts — walked on the bleak and barren moon between 1969 and 1972 in Project Apollo. They scouted areas from the relatively smooth Sea of Tranquility to a mountain-ringed valley named Taurus-Littrow. The final three teams drove over wide areas in wire-wheeled moon buggies.

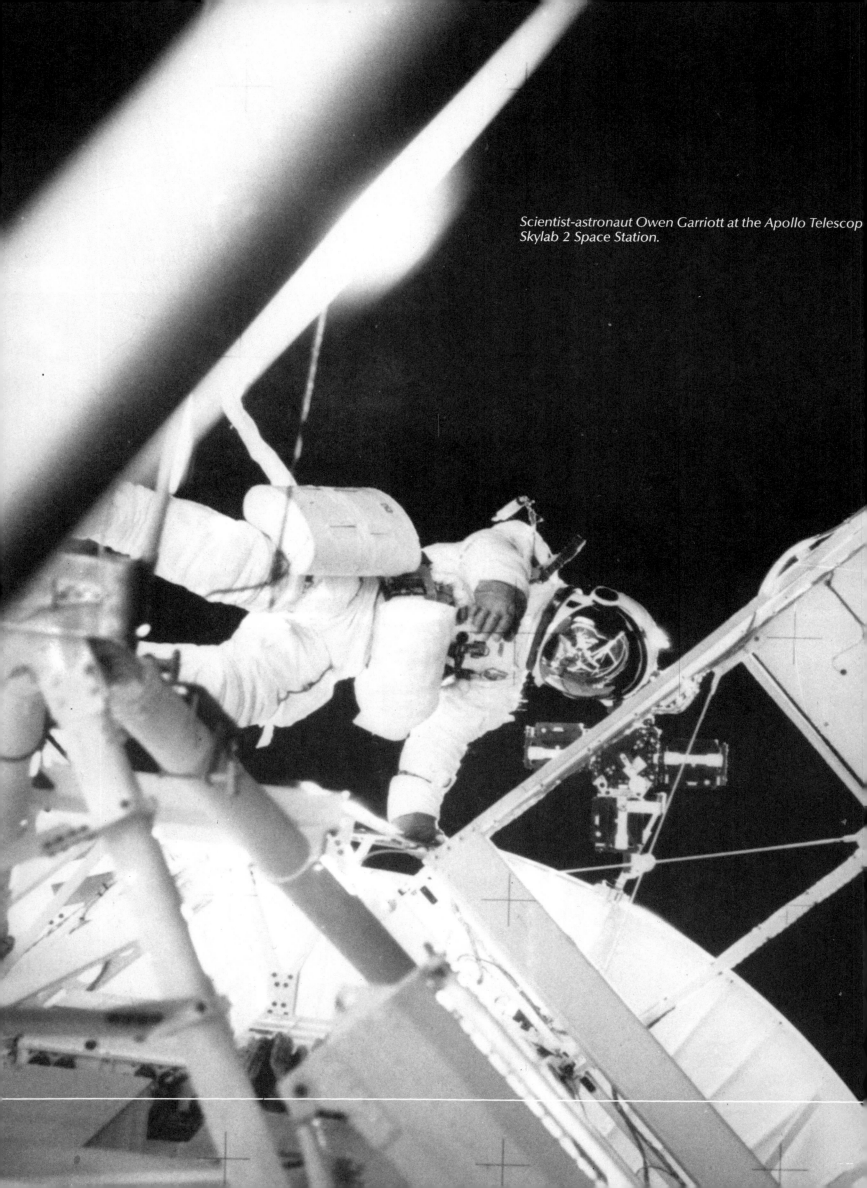

Scientist-astronaut Owen Garriott at the Apollo Telescop
Skylab 2 Space Station.

nt of the

DISCOVERY
AND EXPLORATION

The moon was just the beginning.

Humans had spent their first four or five milleniums establishing the dimensions of a single planet — Earth. In just one generation, space technology allowed the exploration of other worlds of the solar system, and we have learned some wondrous things.

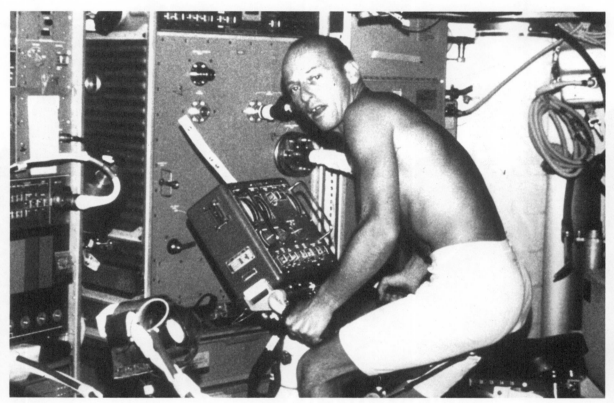

Skylab pilot Paul Weitz mans the control and display panel for the Apollo Telescope Mount during Skylab mission.

Skylab commander Charles Conrad works out on an ergometer, a bicycle-like device, to keep in shape during 1973 mission.

An artist's concept of the Pioneer spacecraft for the "grand tour" fly-by scientific-photographic mission.

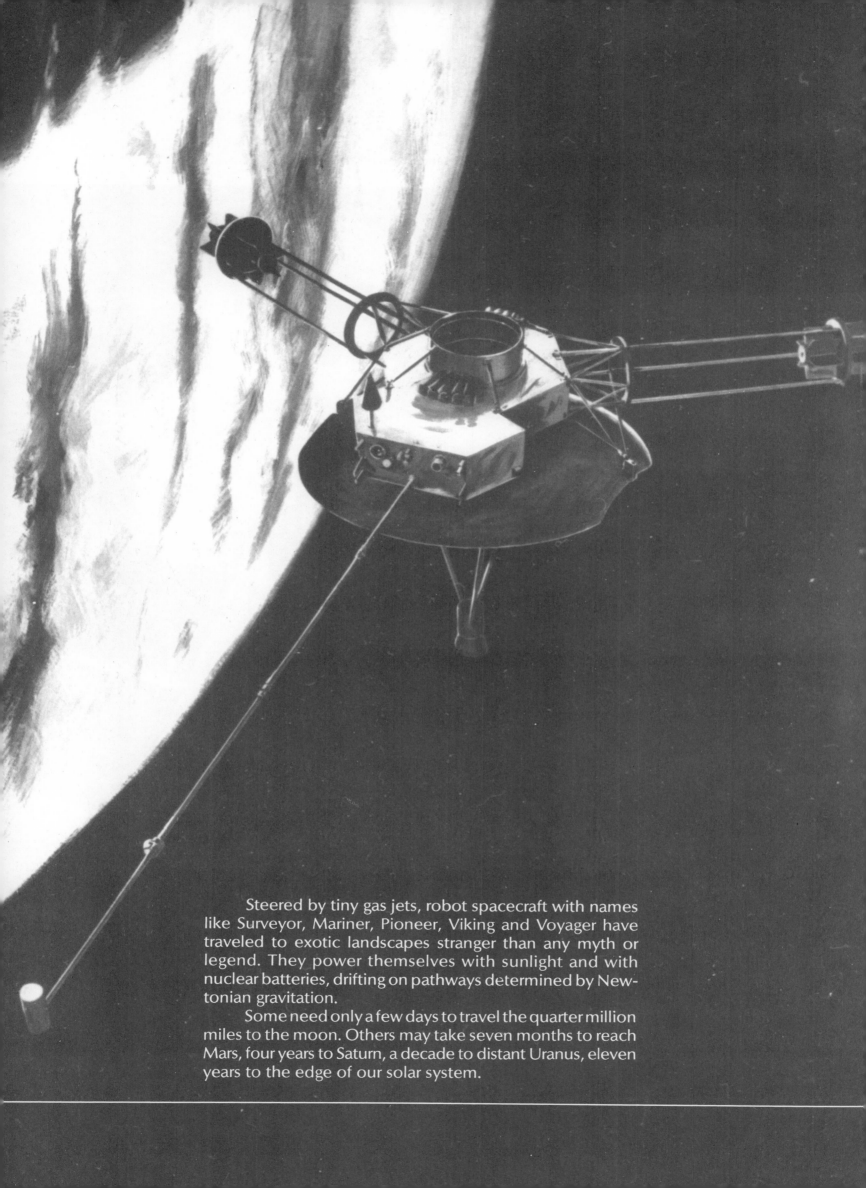

Steered by tiny gas jets, robot spacecraft with names like Surveyor, Mariner, Pioneer, Viking and Voyager have traveled to exotic landscapes stranger than any myth or legend. They power themselves with sunlight and with nuclear batteries, drifting on pathways determined by Newtonian gravitation.

Some need only a few days to travel the quarter million miles to the moon. Others may take seven months to reach Mars, four years to Saturn, a decade to distant Uranus, eleven years to the edge of our solar system.

A NASA drawing showing how the Viking lander spacecraft would be deployed after landing on Mars.

At their destinations, some skim close, snapping pictures and gathering a few days of data before soaring toward another planet or into interstellar space. Some orbit their targets to examine them at length, while others descend to the surface to probe the mysteries there.

What they collect is flashed as binary bits to Earth computers which translate the unknown into recognizable places filled with surprises and secrets. Vague speculations of the past have been replaced by solid scientific findings.

Far left: *Drawing of "Counter-Moon," the third mission of Boeing's Program for Astronomical Research and Scientific Experiments Concerning Space. It would follow the establishment of a moon colony.*

As a result, we have caught the first views of the great storm systems and rings of Jupiter; the active volcanoes on its salt-covered moon, Io; the parched and cratered wasteland of Mercury; ancient river bottoms, raging winds and a volcano fifteen miles high on Mars; sulfuric acid clouds, lightning, an active volcano and hellish temperatures on Venus; the thousand rings and tantalizing moons of Saturn, and at least forty stars that may be the centers of solar systems like our own.

Because it was our nearest neighbor, the moon was the first objective of our probes. And when President Kennedy committed American astronauts to land on its surface, that effort was accelerated in order to find safe areas to touch down. A series of Ranger spacecraft crashed into the lunar surface, snapping thousands of photos up to the moment of impact. Lunar Orbiter spacecraft circled the moon with their cameras, and the spider-like Surveyor soft-landed on the surface to test its firmness.

The moon explorers returned to Earth with a total of 843 pounds of lunar rocks and soil. They left behind science recorders that sent information back for several years on moonquakes, meteor hits, radiation and the solar wind.

Scientists have analyzed only a fraction of the moon rock treasure. Much of it has been stored in vaccum vaults, awaiting the day, perhaps years from now, when better diagnostic tools and techniques are developed.

But already the study is providing clues to the early history of our moon, our Earth and our solar system.

Emerging is a picture of a moon that was born in searing heat, lived a brief life of boiling lava and shattering collision, then died geologically in an early, primitive stage.

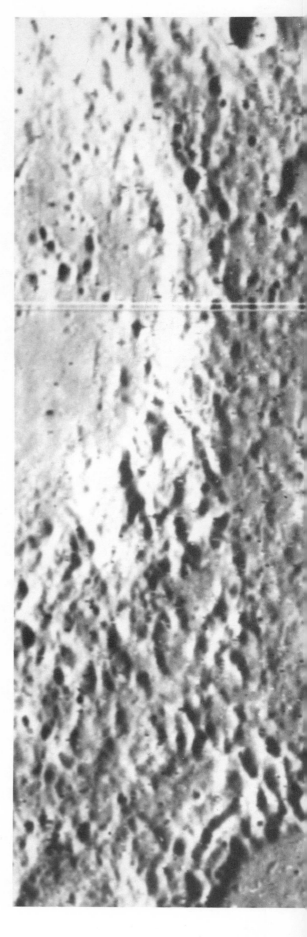

Mariner 10 took this picture of Mercury from an altitude of 21,700 miles, in 1974.

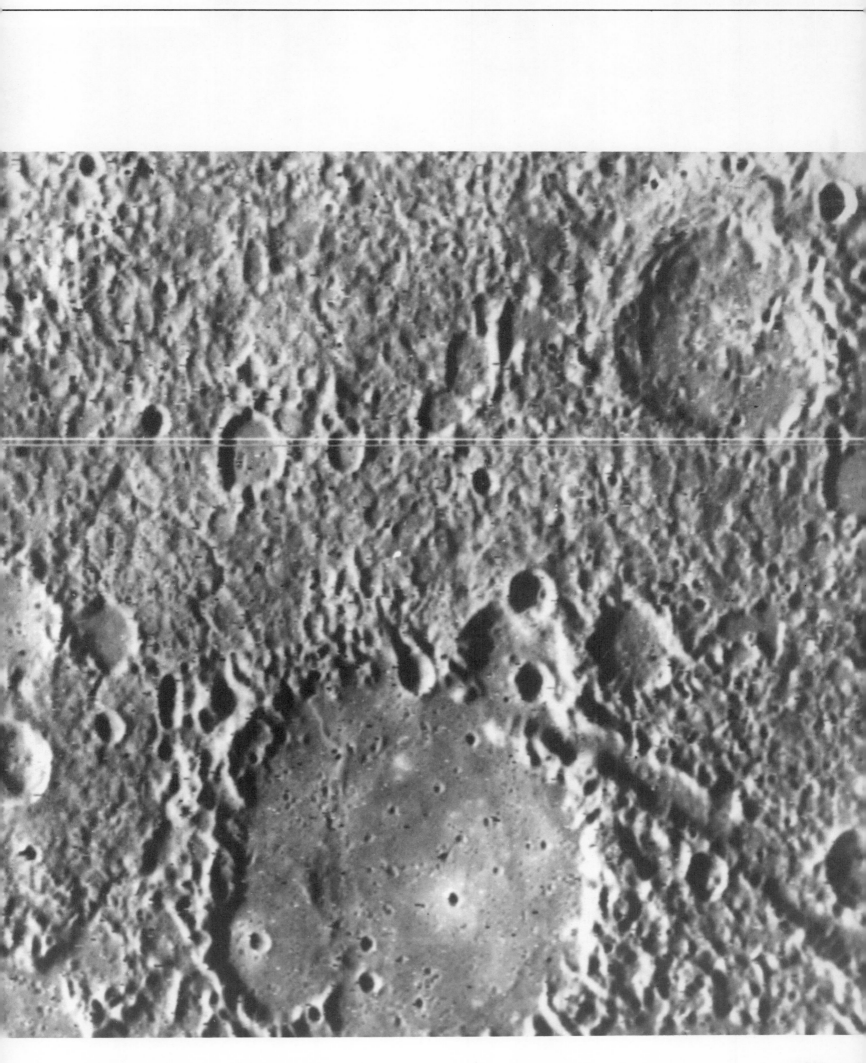

Mariner 10 is launched for a trip to the planets in 1973.

Voyager is launched on a mission to the outer planets, in September 1977.

Even before man landed on the moon, NASA was launching spacecraft to Venus and Mars, and later dispatched probes to Mercury, Jupiter and Saturn.

From these flights NASA is assembling a vast informational mosaic about the solar system and its intricate workings. A basic goal — as in the study of the moon — is to learn more about planet Earth, fitting it into the cosmic puzzle that is the origin, evolution and the structure of the universe.

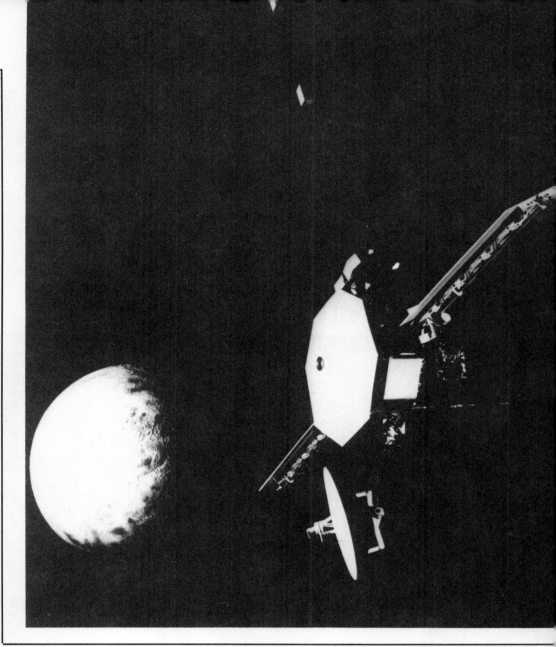

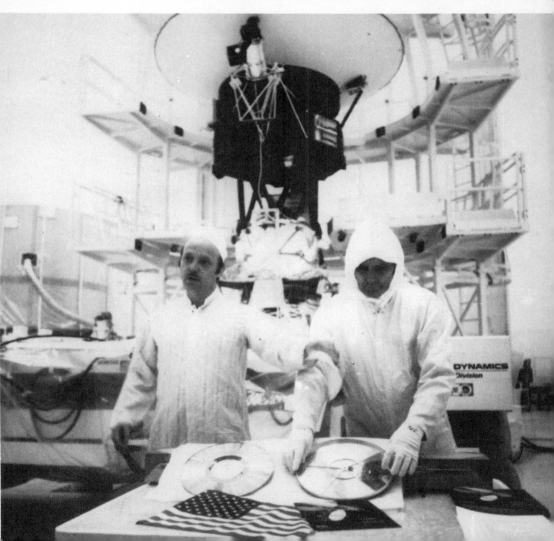

Upper Right: *In simulation, Mariner 10 is shown in fly-by to Venus.*

A digital record and an American flag are prepared for storage aboard Voyager 2.

Some astronomers believe, for example, that Mars may today represent an earlier evolutionary state of Earth when its atmosphere was being formed, and that Venus may represent what would happen to the Earth if its surface temperature were to rise significantly.

More recent discoveries have come from a far-off realm, Saturn, relayed by Voyagers 1 and 2, a pair of marvelous machines that earlier probed Jupiter. These twins beamed back data and images in 1980 and 1981 that taxed the imagination.

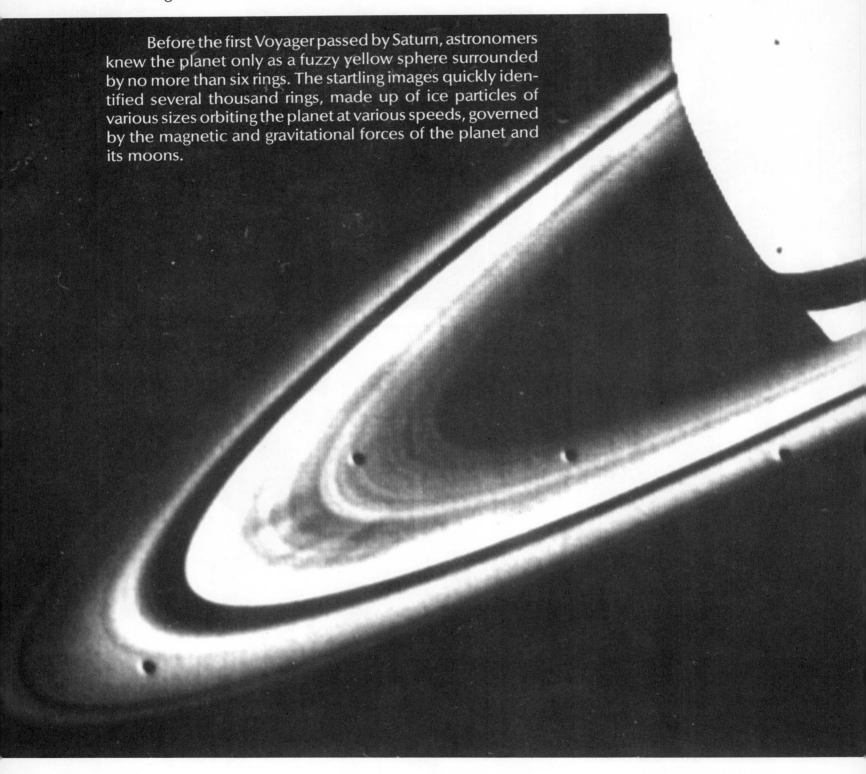

Before the first Voyager passed by Saturn, astronomers knew the planet only as a fuzzy yellow sphere surrounded by no more than six rings. The startling images quickly identified several thousand rings, made up of ice particles of various sizes orbiting the planet at various speeds, governed by the magnetic and gravitational forces of the planet and its moons.

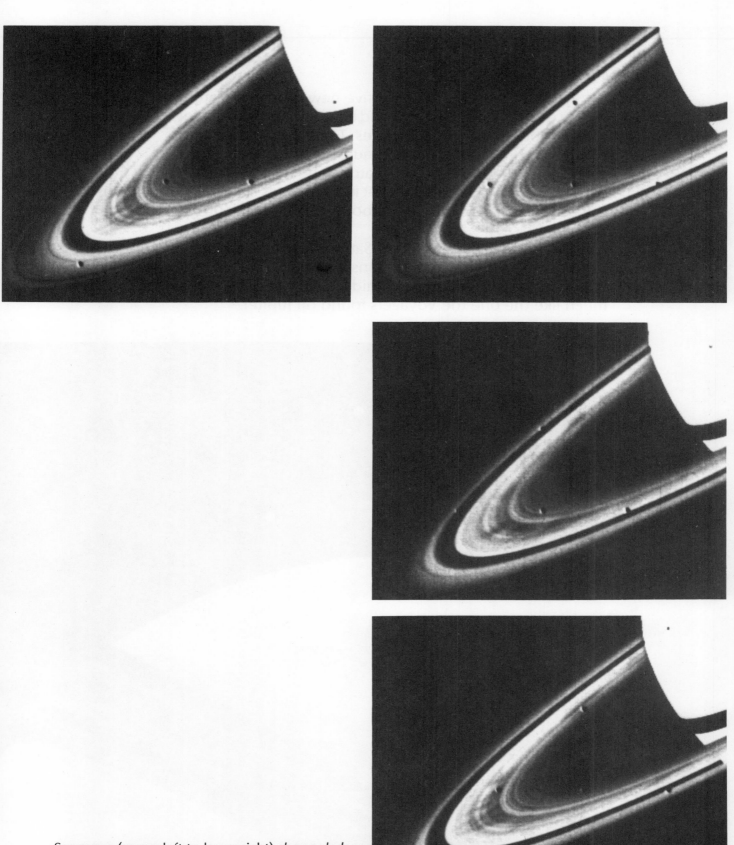

Sequence (upper left to lower right) *shows dark, spokelike features in Saturn's rings revolving around the planet.*

The Voyagers discovered five new moons of Saturn, raising the total to seventeen, and learned some fascinating things about these orbiting bodies. Titan, the largest moon, received the most attention, because it is the only one in the solar system known to have an atmosphere. However, it is inconceivable that life could exist in the oceans of liquid nitrogen and freezing hydrocarbons believed to be on Titan's surface.

The spacecraft also found Saturn's atmosphere of hydrogen and helium alive with monster storms, with winds of 900 miles an hour whipping its midsection — a pattern very much like the one the Voyagers found on Jupiter.

Saturn and two of its moons, Tethys and Dione (left), were photographed by Voyager I from eight million miles on November 3, 1980.

The night side of Saturn's moon, Titan, was photographed from a range of 563,000 miles by Voyager 2 in 1981.

Pioneer photographed Saturn's moon, Titan, for the first time in 1979.

Pioneer Venus-A is launched on its way to Venus.

American spacecraft have discovered other beauties, mysteries and realities in their journeys among the planets.

They found that Venus, Earth's nearest planetary neighbor, is a blistering hot world where 900-degree heat is trapped in a thick atmosphere of carbon dioxide laden with sulfuric acid clouds. The carbon dioxide is vented from volcanoes, creating a greenhouse effect. A valley - 950 miles long, 125 feet wide and three miles deep - may have been created by tension in the planet's crust pulling at the surface. Scattered across the landscape are huge circular depressions unlike anything seen elsewhere in the solar system. Some are hundreds of miles across and they have scores of concentric, ridgelike rings.

Venus, as seen by the Pioneer spacecraft.

Venus, as photographed by Mariner 10 on February 9, 1974.

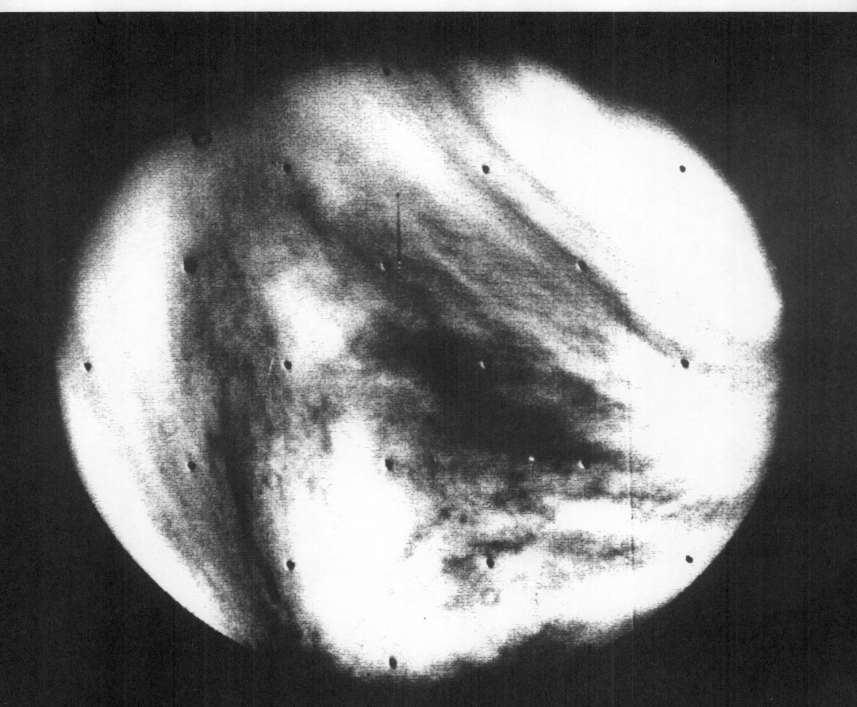

Mariner 10.

Mercury has a weak magnetic field and its airless surface is pocked with millions of craters, some up to 160 miles
wide. From a distance, parts of the planet look like a wrin-
kled prune. It shows evidence of heavy volcanic activity
early in its history, but today it is a dead planet.

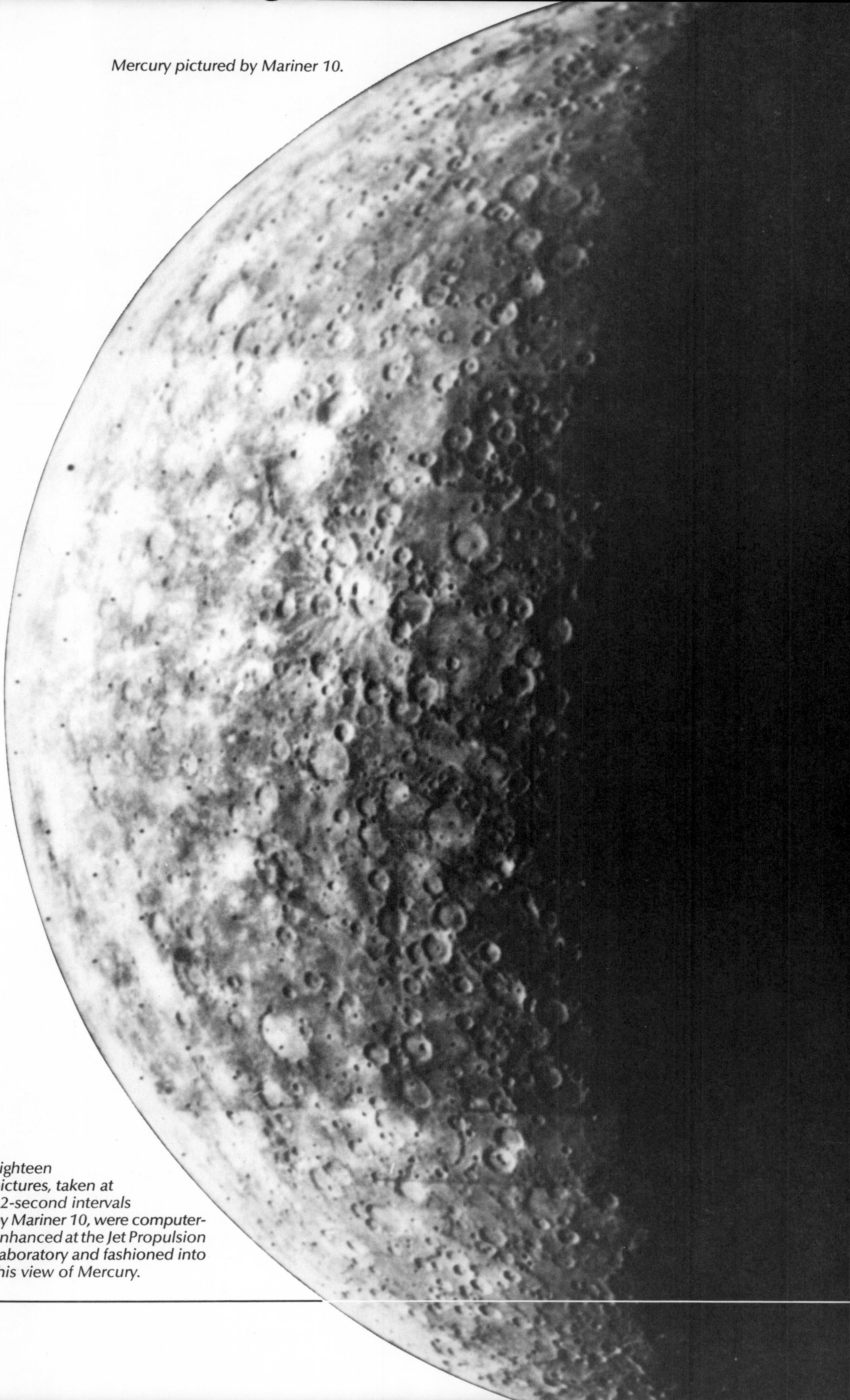

Mercury pictured by Mariner 10.

*Eighteen
pictures, taken at
42-second intervals
by Mariner 10, were computer-
enhanced at the Jet Propulsion
Laboratory and fashioned into
this view of Mercury.*

A Viking spacecraft blasts off for a trip to Mars in 1975.

Mars is a remarkably diverse planet, far different than astronomers ever imagined. It gets its name, the red planet, because its soil is rich in rust. Dust covers the surface under a sparse atmosphere that allows wind to stir up monstrous storms, some growing to such proportions that they blanket the entire planet. Massive volcanoes dot the landscape, and dry, sinuous channels, perhaps once carved by flowing water, stretch for hundreds of miles. Though Mars once may have had water, temperatures and atmospheric pressures are now so low that water can exist only as vapor or ice. Some scientists wonder whether Mars harbors any form of life, but two Viking craft that landed there in 1975 found no sign of any in the limited areas they explored.

Photo of Mars taken by Viking Orbiter 1 shows a shock wave or weather front (center right) *and a volcano* (left).

Viking's view of the rocky Martian plain.

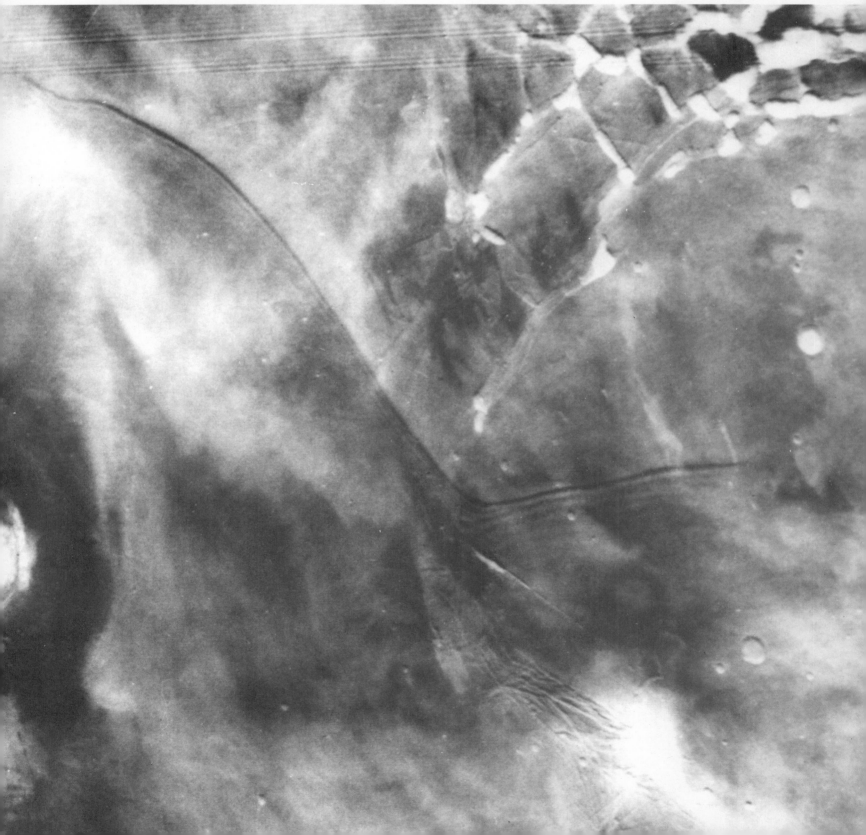

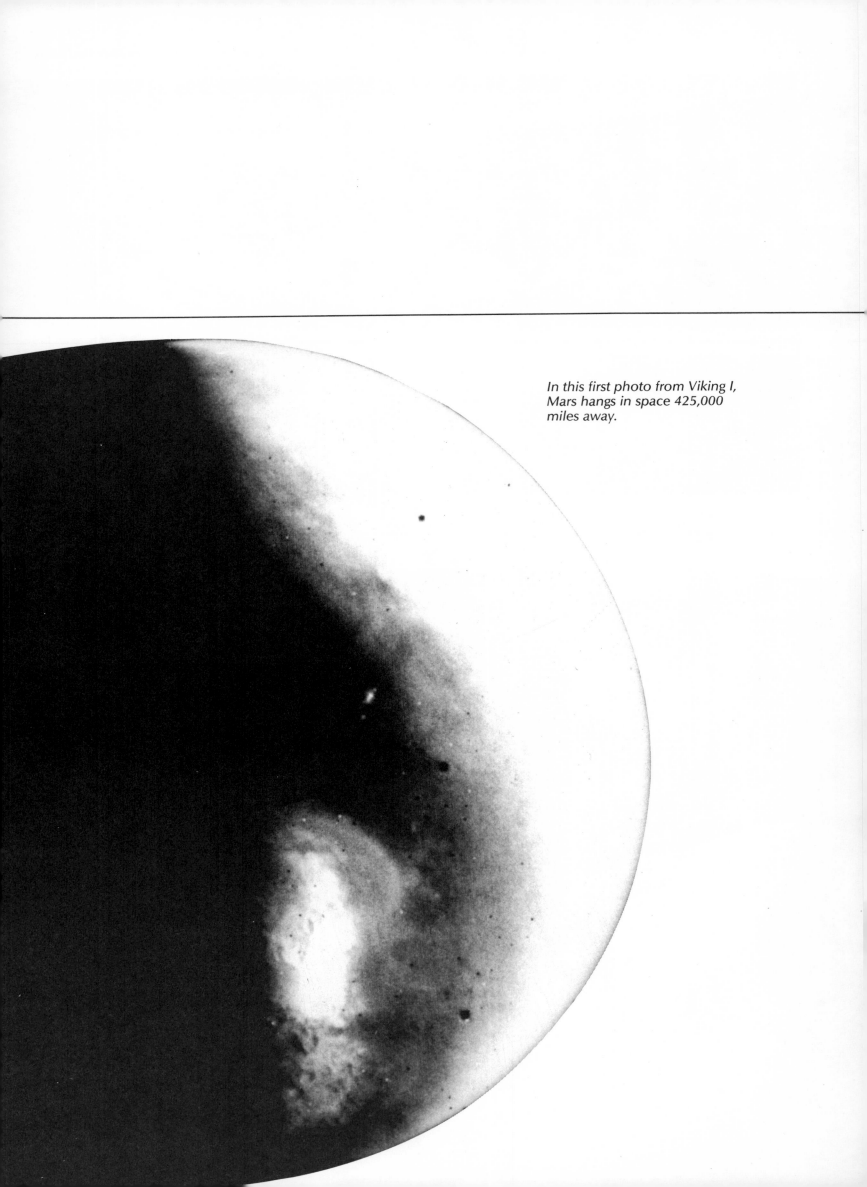

In this first photo from Viking I, Mars hangs in space 425,000 miles away.

The second Viking spacecraft is launched on its way to Mars.

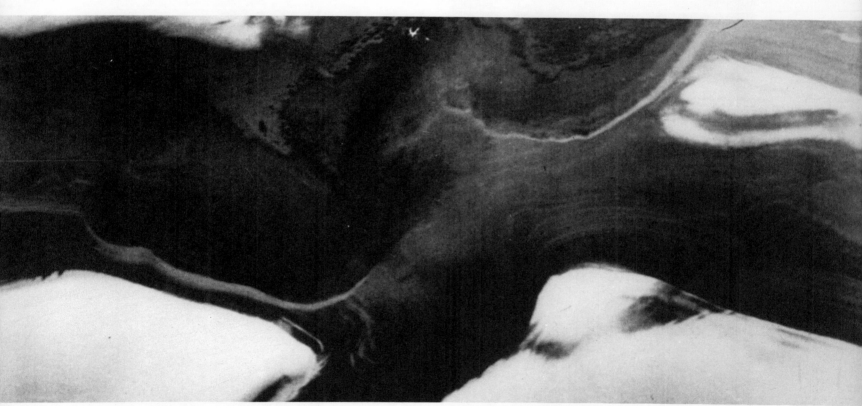

A view near Mars' north pole, taken by Viking Orbiter 2.

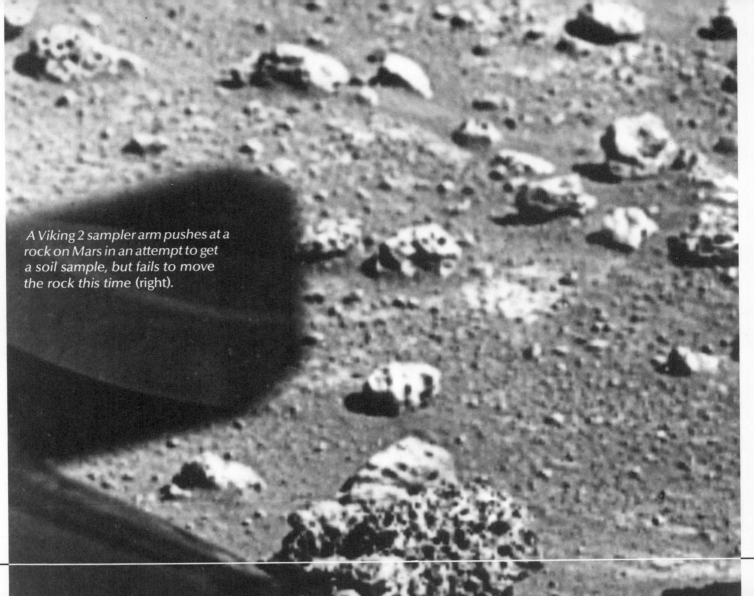

A Viking 2 sampler arm pushes at a rock on Mars in an attempt to get a soil sample, but fails to move the rock this time (right).

Jupiter is the largest planet in the solar system, and a valuable astronomical laboratory because of the diversity of its system of at least fifteen moons. Its four major moons bear the same relationship to their planet as the planets do to the sun. The nearest is almost solid rock, like Mercury, the closest planet to the sun. The farthest away is a slush ball, with a rock in the center, like gaseous Jupiter. The Voyagers discovered a ring around Jupiter and three new moons.

A rectified Pioneer 11 photo from telemetry data shows Jupiter's great red spot.

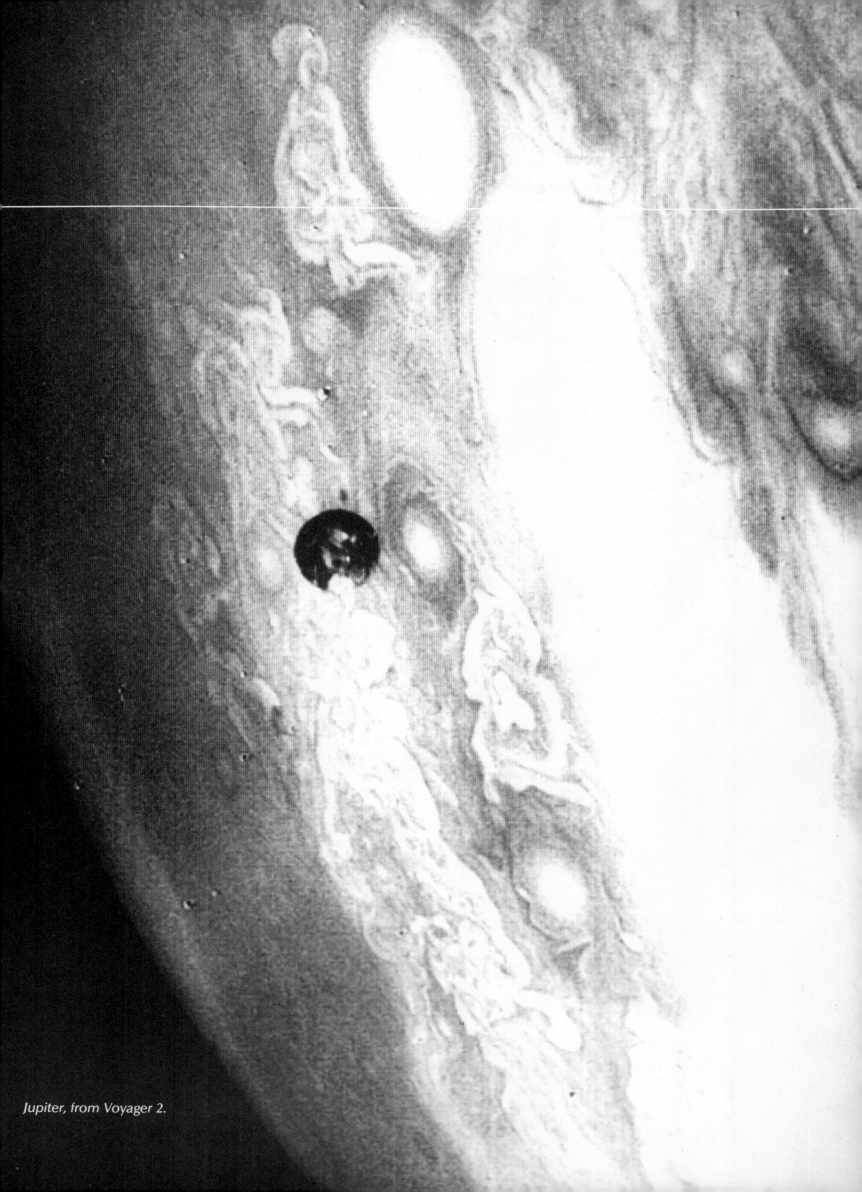

Jupiter, from Voyager 2.

The southern hemisphere of the planet Jupiter shows the great red spot, photographed by Voyager 2.

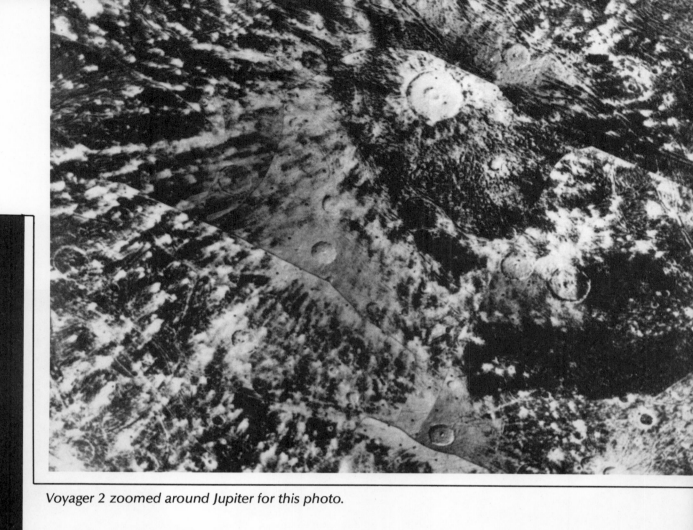

Voyager 2 zoomed around Jupiter for this photo.

An image of Io, Jupiter's moon, made by Voyager 1 in 1979.

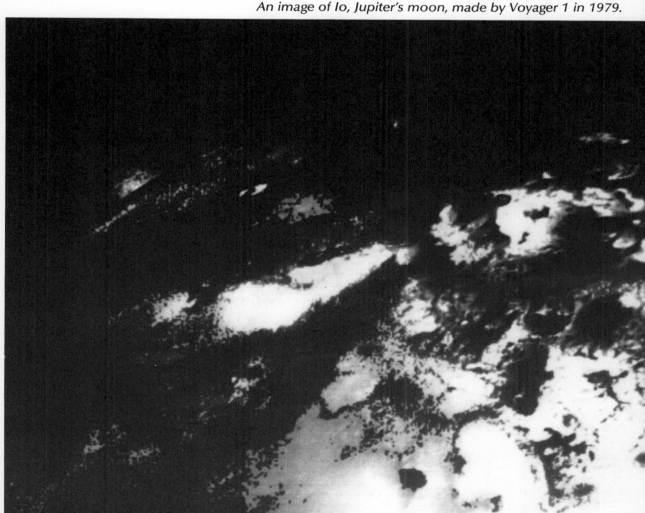

A "family portrait" of Uranus' five largest moons,
compiled from images sent back January 20, 1986 by
the Voyager 2 spacecraft.

MIRANDA   ARIEL   U M

We found new rings and ten tiny moons around Uranus,
the third largest planet, 1.8 billion miles away.

Voyager 2 photo of two moons associated with rings of Uranus, taken at a
distance of 2.5 million miles January 21, 1986.

TITANIA

OBERON

EL

1986U8

1986U7

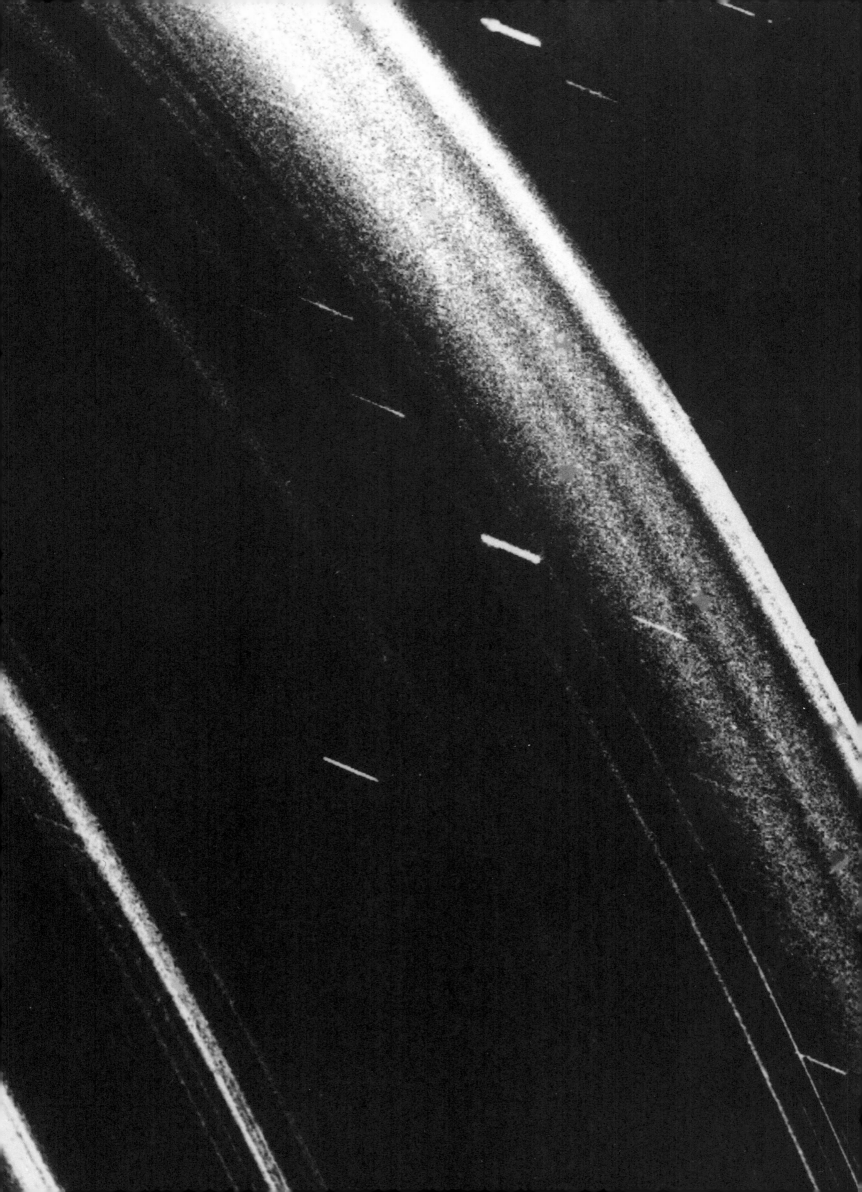

This dramatic Voyager 2 photo shows a continuous distribution of small particles throughout the Uranus ring system.

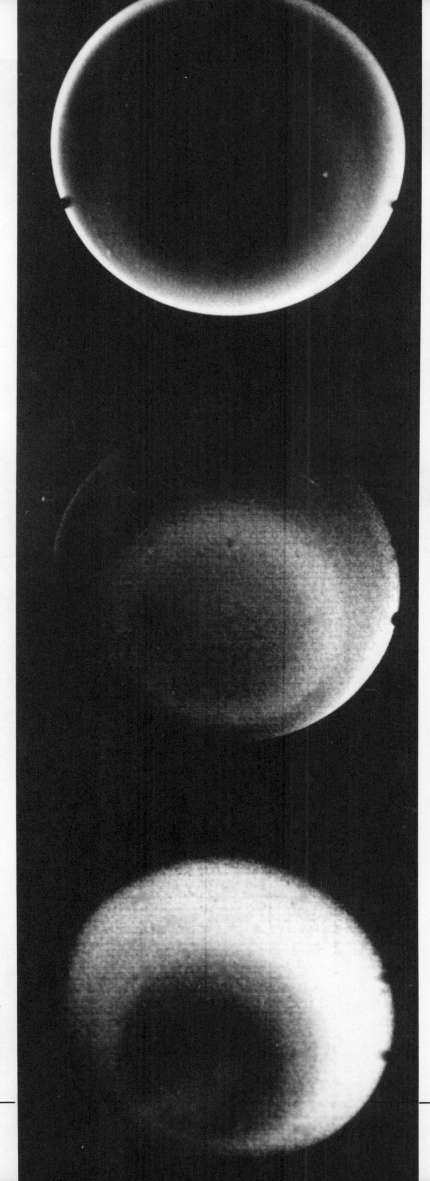

Three photos of Uranus show the varying appearance of the planet from Voyager 2.

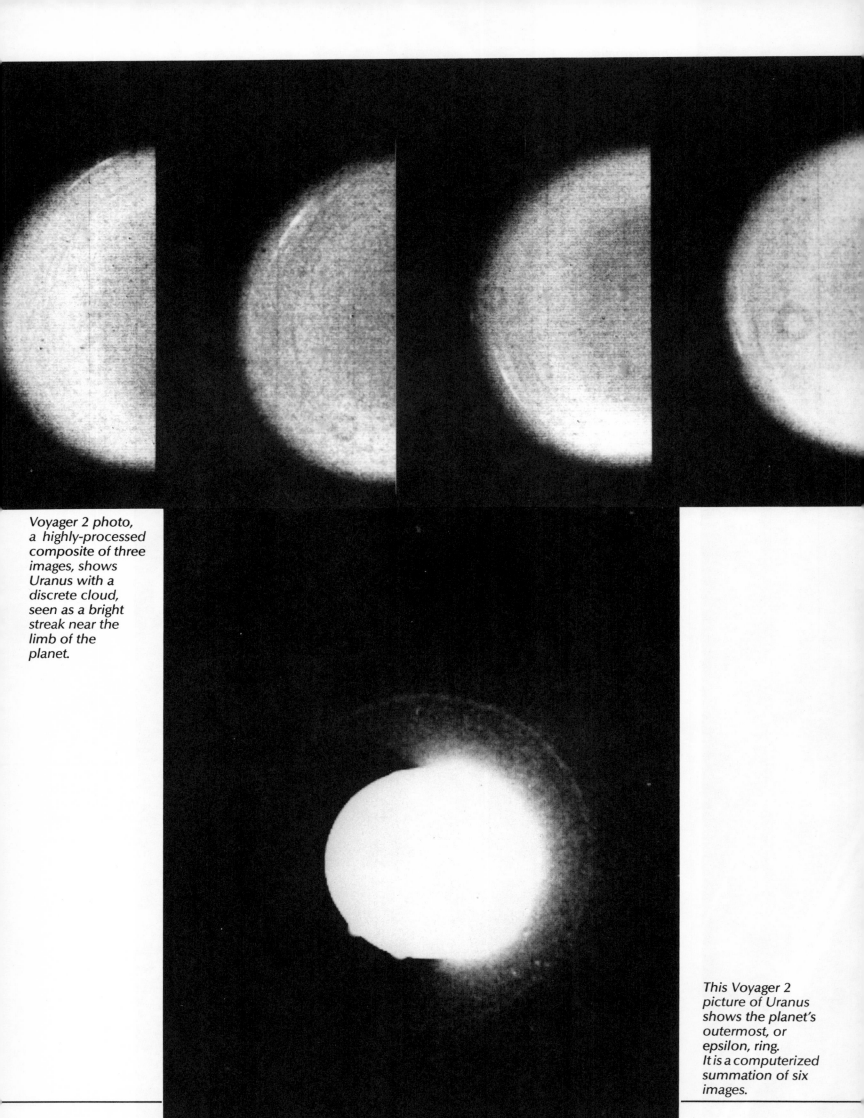

Voyager 2 photo, a highly-processed composite of three images, shows Uranus with a discrete cloud, seen as a bright streak near the limb of the planet.

This Voyager 2 picture of Uranus shows the planet's outermost, or epsilon, ring. It is a computerized summation of six images.

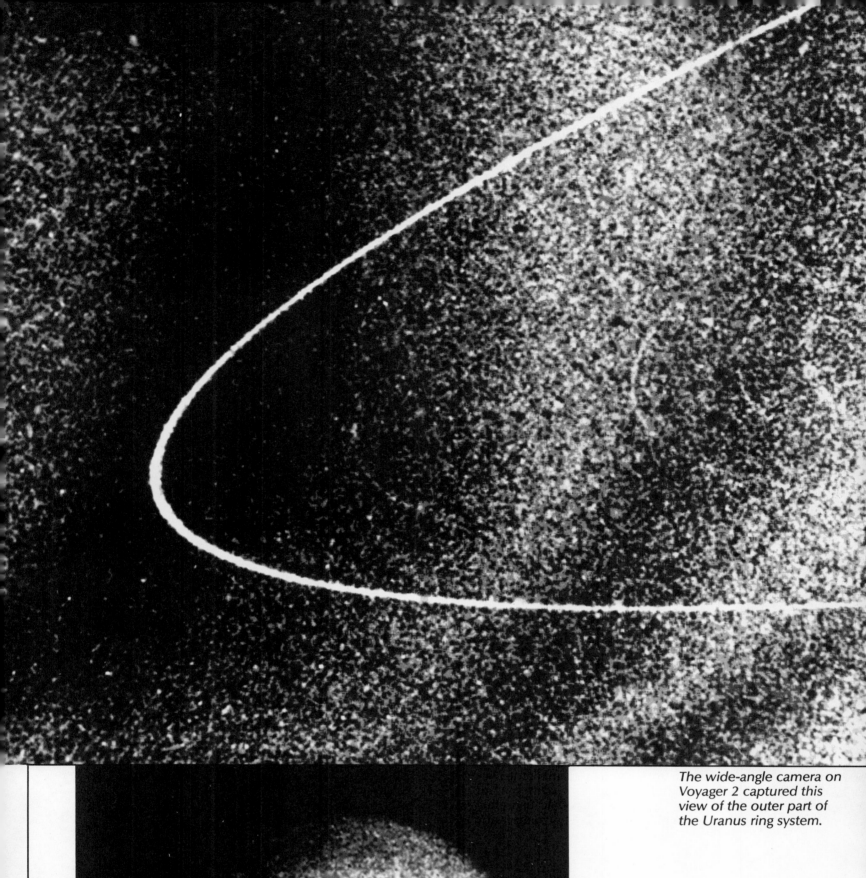

The wide-angle camera on Voyager 2 captured this view of the outer part of the Uranus ring system.

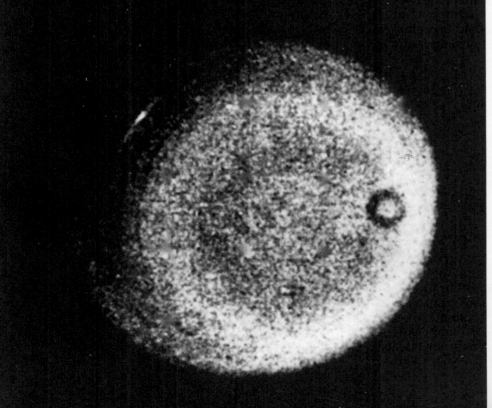

The Voyager project, managed for NASA by the Jet Propulsion Laboratory, provided these time-lapse images of Uranus, showing the movement of two small, bright, streaky clouds.

A high-resolution composite of Titania, one of the large moons of Uranus, was made from Voyager 2 images taken January 24, 1986.

A composite photo of Miranda, a Uranus satellite, taken by Voyager 2.

A composite photo shows
the complex terrain of Ariel,
a Uranian moon.

The southern hemisphere of
Umbriel, the darkest
of Uranus' larger moons,
displays heavy cratering.

And there are more things to see. Robot explorers are moving on, heading for Neptune and into the netherland beyond our star system — into the deeper unknown.

Pioneer 10 has been charting that region. On June 13, 1983, after a journey of eleven years and 3½ billion miles, the tiny spacecraft became the first manmade object to leave the solar system and enter the realm of the stars.

The durable robot, designed to last only two years — long enough to probe Jupiter — was still transmitting as it crossed the orbit of Neptune, at the outermost planet. Normally, Pluto is the farthest planet from the sun, but at times, Neptune's path gives it that honor.

A major surprise of Pioneer's voyage was the discovery that the boundary of the sun's atmosphere, or heliosphere, is much farther out than supposed. Many scientists had expected it to end near Jupiter's orbit. But even after leaving the solar system Pioneer's instruments showed no decline in the heliosphere's strength, only what seems to be a swelling and contraction connected with cycles of solar activity.

Clearly, these amazing spacecraft have produced a revolution in our concept of the solar system and the Earth's place in it. Most outstanding is the incredible diversity of the planets and moons they have inspected. Each is a unique body.

The findings have answered a lot of questions, but they have raised many others. So the quest will continue, with the United States planning in the next decade to dispatch even more sophisticated robots to probe Venus, Mars and Jupiter. Ultimately, man himself may explore these sister worlds.

The space age is little more than a quarter century old and America alone has spent more than $160 billion on its programs. What return has there been on that investment? Some estimates place the return at between $6 and $7 for every dollar spent.

America originally went into space for political reasons, as a response to Russia's Sputnik. But, from the very beginning space technology quickly mushroomed from a Cold War prestige contest into an ever-growing multi-billion-dollar market for hardware and services. It has spurred new industries, and, in the process, hundreds of thousands of jobs and skilled people.

The technology of Apollo and other programs — computers, electronics, metals — has found its way into medicine, communications, transportation, industrial processes, public safety, construction, home appliances, recreation and food products.

Satellites have revolutionized global communications, maritime navigation, worldwide weather forecasting and our knowledge of earth and its resources.

Medicine has benefitted greatly from space technology. Pacemakers and other implantable heart aids are spinoffs from miniaturized heart circuitry. So are fast, accurate diagnostic machines for many diseases. Because of small sensors developed to monitor the physical condition of astronauts in space, a single nurse seated at a console can remotely check the conditions of several patients simultaneously.

Shuttle Columbia, with chase plane, approaches landing at Edwards Air Force Base, California.

SPACE SHUTTLE PROGRAM

The space shuttle, a NASA official once said, is a "great white bird that breathes of the future." The shuttle is indeed a remarkable machine that is revolutionizing the way humans are exploring and doing business in space. Yet, its full potential is yet to be realized.

Astronauts John W. Young (left) and Robert L. Crippen with model of shuttle Columbia.

Columbia blasts off on first reuseable shuttle flight, April 12, 1981.

Columbia perches on Pad 39A, undergoing tests before April 1981 launch.

Space shuttle Columbia rides piggyback aboard a NASA 747 jet after being ferried from California to the space center in Florida.

Spectators at Kennedy Space Center follow Columbia's path.

Space shuttle Columbia liftoff.

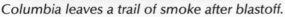

Columbia leaves a trail of smoke after blastoff.

The era of the reuseable spaceship began April 12, 1981, when the first shuttle, Columbia, roared from Cape Canaveral, Florida with veteran John Young and a rookie, Robert Crippen, at the controls.

147

Don Puddy, entry flight director, sits at console at the Johnson Space Center watching shuttle Columbia land.

Once in orbit, they thoroughly checked Columbia's systems and then opened the clamshell-like doors that cover the shuttle's sixty-foot cargo bay, which can hold up to thirty-three tons of cargo. Operation of the doors is critical, because the inside surfaces function as radiators, ridding the spacecraft of excess heat.

Photo from an NBC-TV monitor shows open doors on shuttle Columbia's cargo bay.

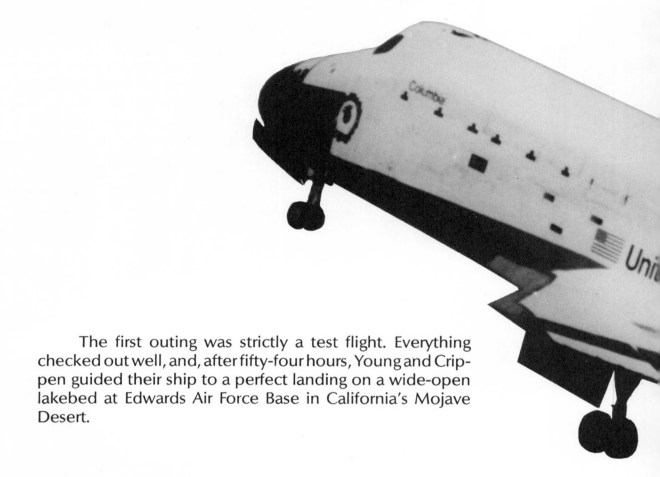

The first outing was strictly a test flight. Everything checked out well, and, after fifty-four hours, Young and Crippen guided their ship to a perfect landing on a wide-open lakebed at Edwards Air Force Base in California's Mojave Desert.

Columbia: touchdown.

(NASA selected the desert for the first few landings to provide plenty of margin for error. The shuttle's main runway is near the launch pad at Cape Canaveral. A California landing meant the shuttle had to be transported back to the launch site locked on top of a modified Boeing 747 jetliner. That adds several days to the turnaround time in preparing a ship for its next launch. Which is why NASA wants to land in Florida.)

Reports from the Columbia crew reflected the near-perfection of that exciting first shuttle flight.

Young, after reaching orbit: "The vehicle is performing just like a champ."

Crippen: "I had a thrill from the moment of liftoff."

Crippen, when the payload bay doors opened: "You're missing one fantastic sight."

Young, shortly before re-entry: "The only thing bad is that we're going to have to come down."

Young, after Columbia landed and rolled to a stop: "You can't believe what a flying machine this is. It's really something special."

Three more shuttle test flights were conducted over the next fifteen months to qualify Columbia for operational missions. The second flight, in November 1981, encountered a problem with a power-producing fuel cell and astronauts Joe Engle and Richard Truly came home early, cutting their planned five-day journey in half.

Columbia was back in space again in March 1982, manned by astronauts Jack Lousma and Gordon Fullerton. As they neared the end of their seven-day trip, late winter rains turned the hard-packed desert sands at Edwards into a quagmire, and they landed instead at another wide-open wasteland — on the western edge of New Mexico's White Sands Missile Range.

Columbia's final test flight began three months later, with Thomas Mattingly and Henry Hartsfield in the cockpit. They completed an almost flawless week-long flight, and on July 4, Independence Day, they swooped to a star-spangled landing at Edwards. Leading the cheers of half a million persons on hand was President Ronald Reagan.

Chase plane watches completion of Columbia's first flight.

During a flag-waving ceremony, NASA administrator James Beggs pronounced the shuttle operational, ready to carry cargo and passengers into space on a regular basis.

To underscore that message, the agency dispatched its second shuttle, Challenger, to Cape Canaveral. Hitch-hiking on the back of the Boeing 747, the new ship passed low over the runway where Columbia had just landed, and then above the reviewing stand where Reagan led the crowd in singing "God Bless America!"

Technicians check satellites before launching from fifth shuttle flight in November, 1982.

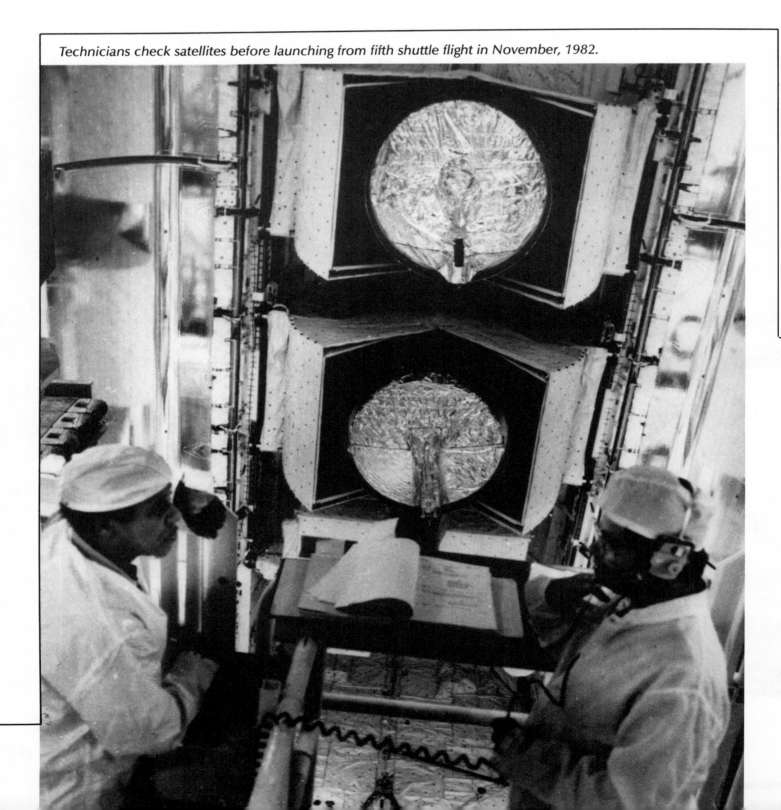

Cargo is loaded aboard shuttle Columbia.

Two other ships, Discovery and Atlantis, joined the fleet in 1984 and 1985.

Space shuttle Discovery in early morning takeoff.

Atlantis, America's fourth shuttle, is readied for 1985 launch.

The world's first manned commercial space transportation service opened for business in November, 1982, when Columbia dashed into orbit with a crew of four and two communications satellites. Telesat of Canada and Satellite Business Systems each paid NASA about $10 million to deliver the satellites. Both were successfully spun out of the cargo bay, and their attached rockets fired to boost them to stationary orbits 22,300 miles high. For a telecast back to earth, the happy crew held up a sign that read, "Ace Moving Co. - We Deliver."

Astronaut Vance Brand holds sign referring to successful deployment of two communications satellites on Columbia flight. Brand is surrounded by (clockwise, left to right) astronauts William Lenoir, Robert Overmyer, and Joseph P. Allen IV.

The Satellite Business Systems spacecraft springs from its protective cradle in the cargo bay of shuttle Columbia.

Astronauts F. Story Musgrave (left) and Donald H. Peterson float about in cargo bay of shuttle Challenger, April 7, 1983.

Challenger made its flight debut in April, 1983. Two of its crew members, Story Musgrave and Donald Peterson, dispatched a Tracking and Data Relay Satellite for NASA. They also took the first space walk in the shuttle program, checking out the space suits and testing tools to be used on later flights.

Spectators watch liftoff of shuttle Challenger from along U.S. 1 in Titusville, Florida.

Liftoff of shuttle Challenger is reflected in canal that runs through Kennedy Space Center launch area.

Challenger crew members (left to right) Dr. Norman Thagard, John Fabian, Dr. Sally Ride, Frederick Hauck, and Robert Crippen, *wave to welcome-home crowd after six-day mission in 1983.*

After sending eighty-two men into space in twenty-two years, the United States finally launched a woman into orbit aboard Challenger on the seventh shuttle mission in June, 1983. Sally Ride was a member of the five person crew. She was one of eight women selected for the astronaut corps in 1978 and 1979.

She and John Fabian were busy the first two days, successfully ejecting commercial communications satellites for Telesat of Canada and the Indonesian government. They then unlimbered the fifty-foot robot arm in the cargo bay to lift an experiment package overboard.

Giant crawler takes Challenger to Pad 39A for its second flight, in 1983.

An Indonesian satellite is deployed from Challenger.

Crew on Challenger's seventh flight (left to right): Norman Thagard, Robert Crippen, Frederick Hauck, Sally Ride and John Fabian.

Astronaut Sally Ride talks with ground controllers from Earth-orbiting Challenger.

The package served as a target for commander Robert Crippen, making his second shuttle flight, and pilot Rick Hauck. They flew above, below and around it to practice space rendezvous techniques. A camera aboard the satellite took dramatic pictures of Challenger in flight. Sally Ride later recaptured the package with the mechanical arm and reberthed it in the bay, for use on a later trip.

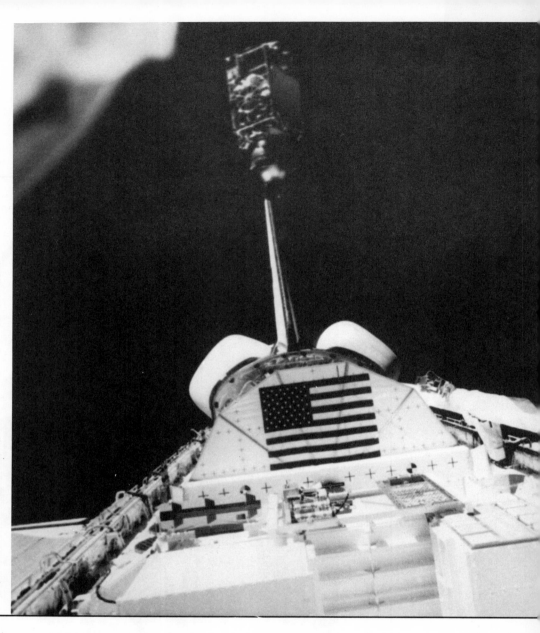

The Indian National Satellite (INSAT) is about to clear the space shuttle Challenger.

Astronaut Guion Bluford checks out an onboard experiment during Challenger's eighth mission.

The shuttle's first night launch took place on the eighth mission, in August, 1983. The spectacular early-morning liftoff was necessary to put Challenger in the proper place at the right time to deploy a communications and weather satelite for the government of India. The five-man crew included America's first black astronaut, Guion Bluford, Jr.

Astronauts Richard Truly and Guion Bluford stretch out for a rest during Challenger flight.

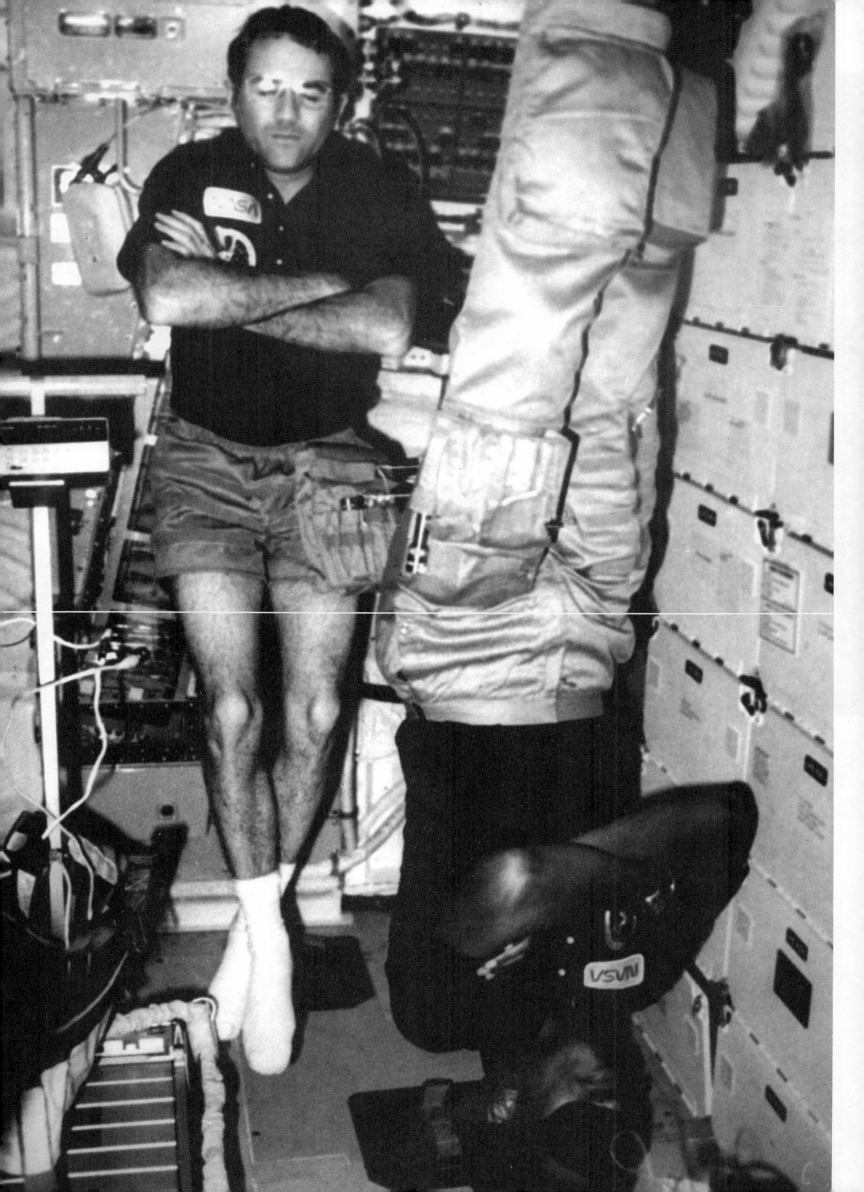

The flight also ended after dark, with the space plane gliding out of a star-filled sky into the glare of hundreds of floodlights at Edwards.

Support units move in as Challenger comes to a stop after night landing at Edwards Air Force Base, California.

Challenger makes its first night landing.

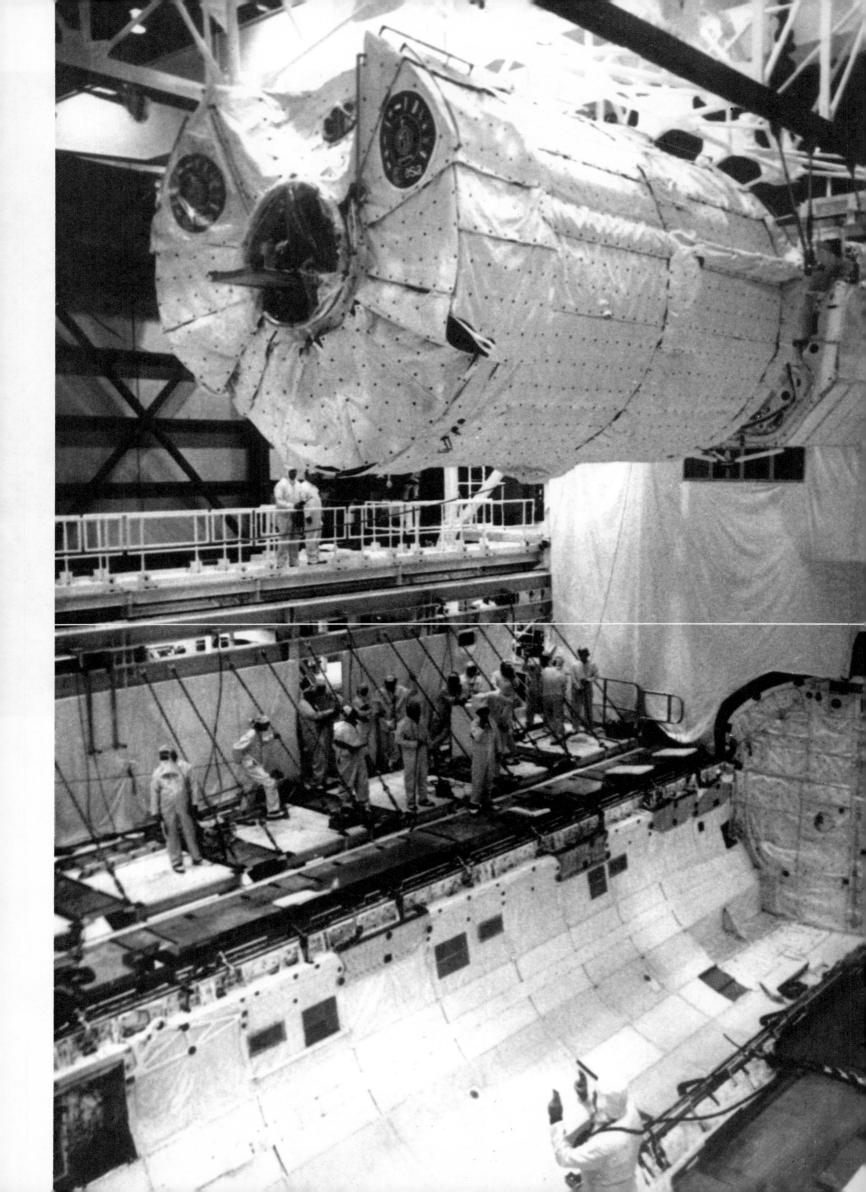

Crew for Challenger's ninth flight: front, Brewster Shaw and John Young; middle, Robert Parker and Ulf Merbold; back, Owen Garriott and Byron Lichtenberg.

An era of shuttle science began in November, 1983, when Columbia soared into space with a sophisticated laboratory called Spacelab in its cargo bay. The six-man crew included the first non-astronauts to fly on a U.S. spaceship. They were Byron Lichtenberg, a biomedical engineer from Massachusetts Institute of Technology, and Ulf Merbold, a West German physicist.

Spacelab, the joint NASA-European Space Agency project, is installed in shuttle Columbia.

Byron Lichtenberg shakes a bottle of fluid in weightlessness experiment aboard Skylab.

The crew worked in round-the-clock, three-man shifts, using the twenty-three-foot-long European-built laboratory for medical, astronomy, earth survey, atmospheric and materials processing experiments. They had planned to stay aloft only nine days, but everything went so well, they remained in space an extra twenty-four hours.

Ulf Merbold, of West Germany, aboard Columbia.

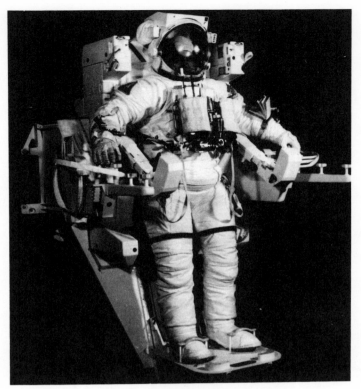

Astronaut Bruce McCandless demonstrates the manned maneuvering unit and its flight support station.

For years, NASA had been developing a back pack—like something Buck Rogers or Flash Gordon might wear — to allow astronauts to fly free of their spaceships, without being attached by a tether. Finally, it was time for the ultimate test, on shuttle flight 10 in February, 1984.

Countdown sign at Kennedy Space Center previews Challenger launch in February, 1984.

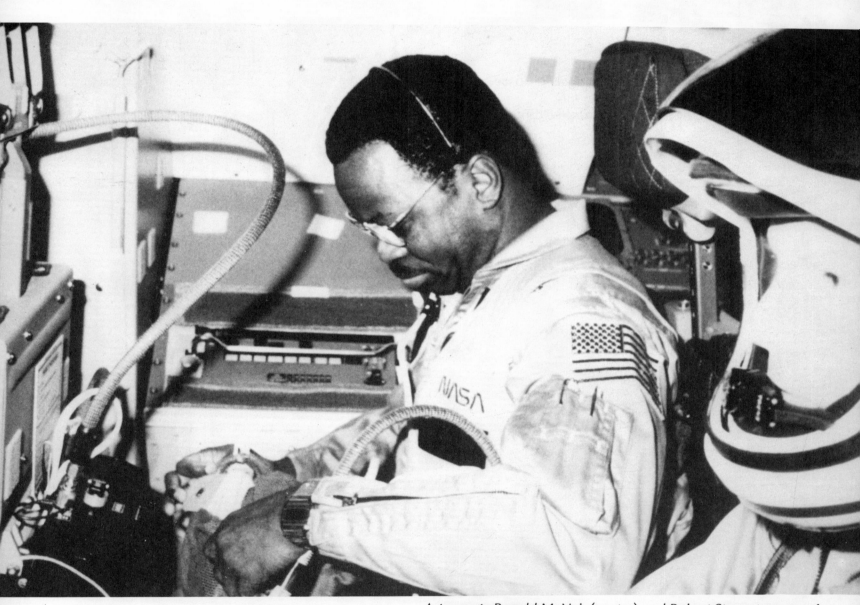

Astronauts Ronald McNair (center) and Robert Stewart prepare for Challenger landing.

Vivid pictures relayed to Earth told the story. Here was a stiff, toy-like figure, appearing to hang suspended in space, silhouetted against a deep black sky, with a bright, cloud-mottled earth curving 150 miles below. This was a man, a human satellite, the first person to fly free in space.

His name was Bruce McCandless II. He moved 320 feet away from Challenger, controlling himself perfectly by triggering small jets that spit bursts of nitrogen gas from the pack on his back. He operated the jet with hand controllers on metal arms extending from the pack.

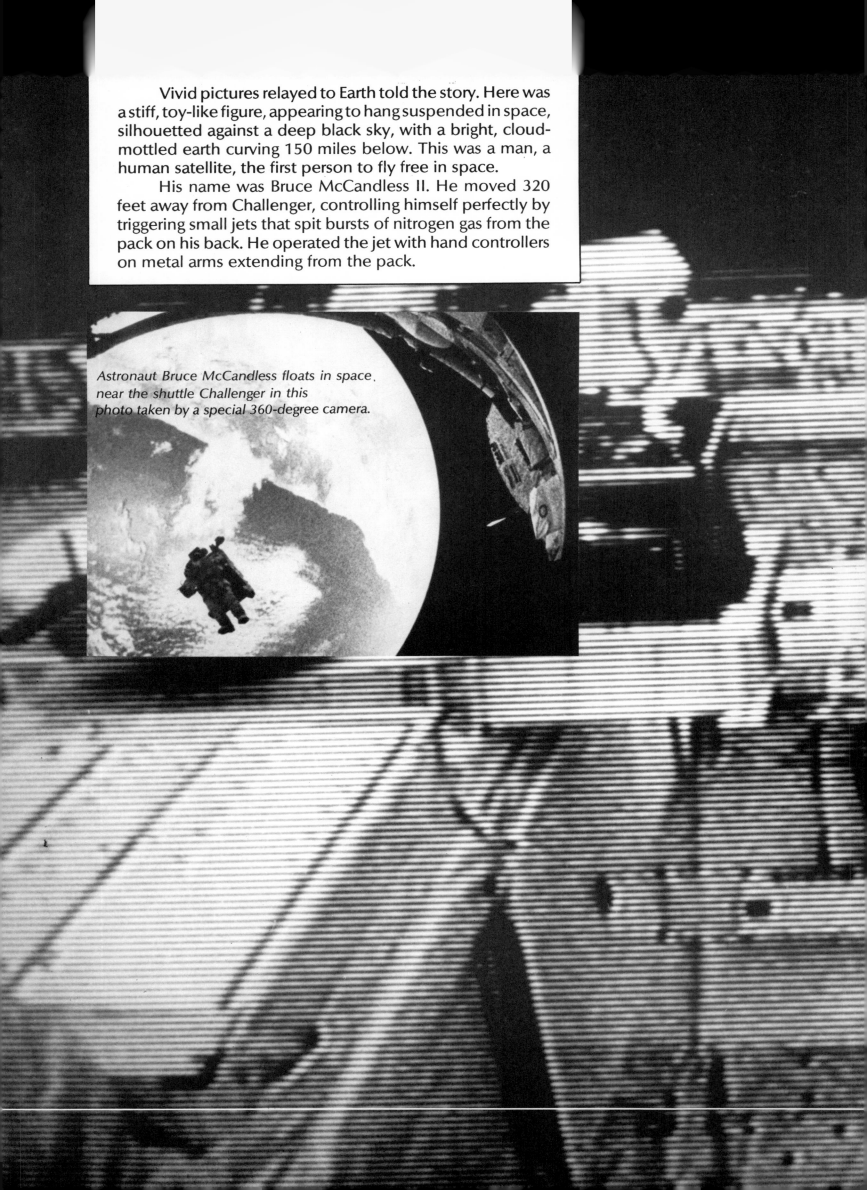

Astronaut Bruce McCandless floats in space near the shuttle Challenger in this photo taken by a special 360-degree camera.

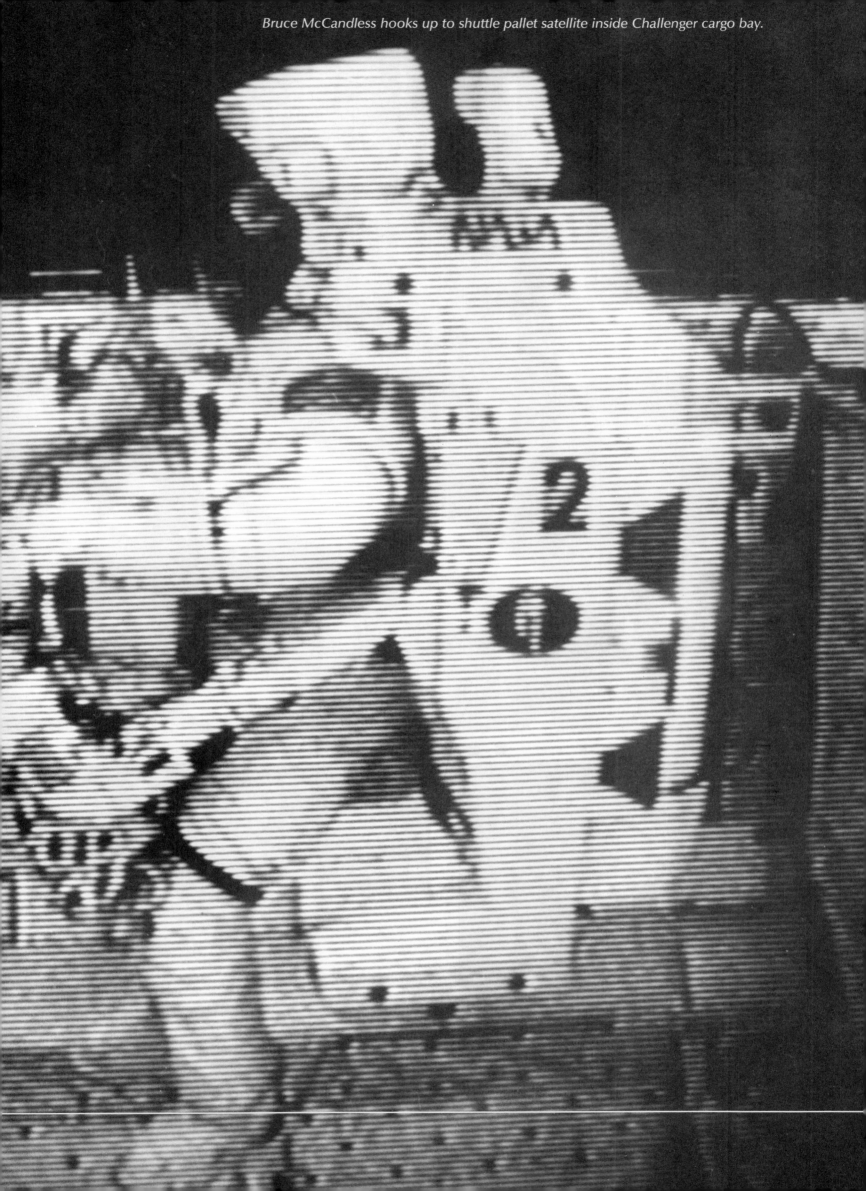

Bruce McCandless hooks up to shuttle pallet satellite inside Challenger cargo bay.

Shuttle Challenger as photographed by astronaut Bruce McCandless as he ventured untethered from the spaceship February 7, 1984.

"Beautiful...Superb...Super!" he kept telling mission control. "We sure have a nice flying machine here."

When he finished, McCandless turned the jet-pack over to fellow space-walker Robert Stewart. Stewart maneuvered the contraption through a series of tests and pronounced it "great."

The crew also deployed two communications satellites and made the first landing on the shuttle runway at Cape Canaveral.

Astronaut Robert Stewart appears to hover over the ocean.

Bruce McCandless, in foot
restraints, rides the Canadian
Arm around the cargo bay to
experiment with "cherry
picker" concept.

Bruce McCandless in Challenger
experiment, February 7, 1984.

Closeup of astronaut Bruce McCandless in space in 1984.

Bruce McCandless uses the remote manipulator system arm and the mobile foot restraint to experiment with "cherry-picker" concept.

Communications satellite Westar after launching from cargo bay of shuttle Challenger.

Palapa satellite, launched February 3, 1984.

Astronaut George Nelson uses the manned maneuvering unit to get a
look at the Solar Maximum Mission Satellite during Challenger flight.

Astronaut George Nelson wore the jet-pack on the next mission leaving the safety of Challenger to fly over to a scientific satellite called Solar Max to try to retrieve it for repair. But a docking device failed to lock on to the satellite, and astronaut Terry Hart finally snagged it with the mechanical arm and placed it in the cargo bay. Nelson and James van Hoften repaired and replaced faulty components in the satellite, and Hart used the arm to return it to orbit, to resume its job of studying the sun.

The umbrella-like Solar Maximum Mission Satellite (SMTS) after deployment April 12, 1984, from the shuttle Challenger.

The giant Long Duration Exposure Facility (LDEF) is suspended on the end of the Canadian Arm of shuttle Challenger, carrying some sixty different experiments.

Ailing Solar Max in the cradle of the cargo bay of Challenger as astronaut James van Hoften rides the "cherry picker," the Canadian Arm.

Astronaut James van Hoften works on faulty attitude control module during the seven-day space mission of shuttle Challenger in 1984.

Astronaut James van Hoften uses power tool to make repairs on Solar Max after it was grappled and placed in cargo bay of shuttle Challenger.

Astronaut George Nelson tries to capture the ailing Solar Max satellite on April 8, 1984.

Challenger astronauts George Nelson (left) and James van Hoften repair ailing satellite, Solar Max.

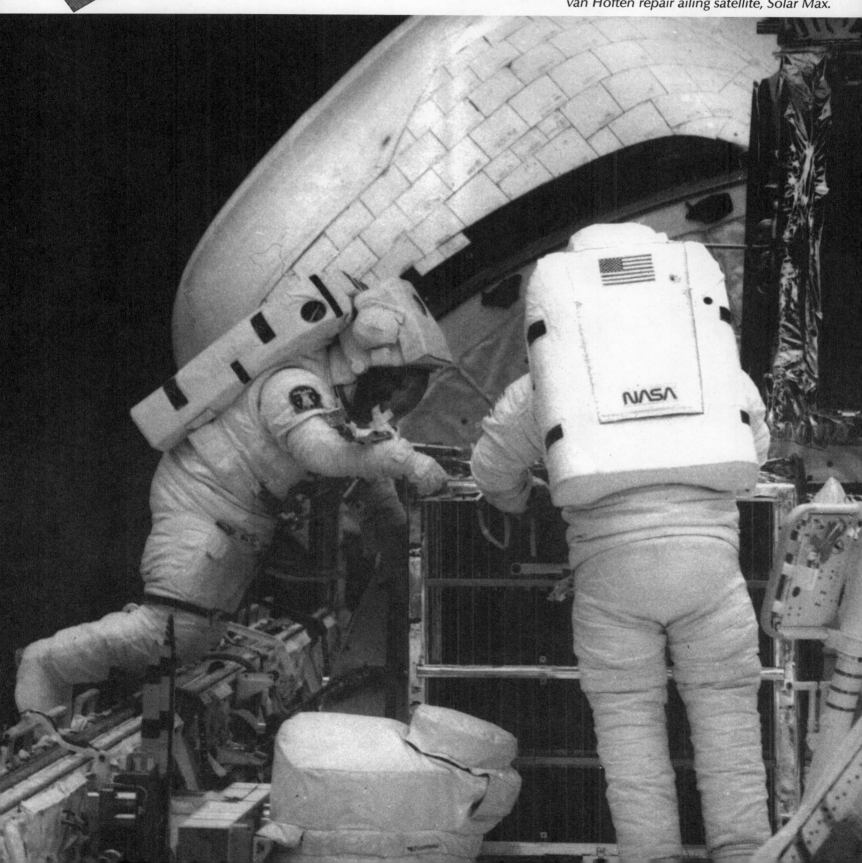

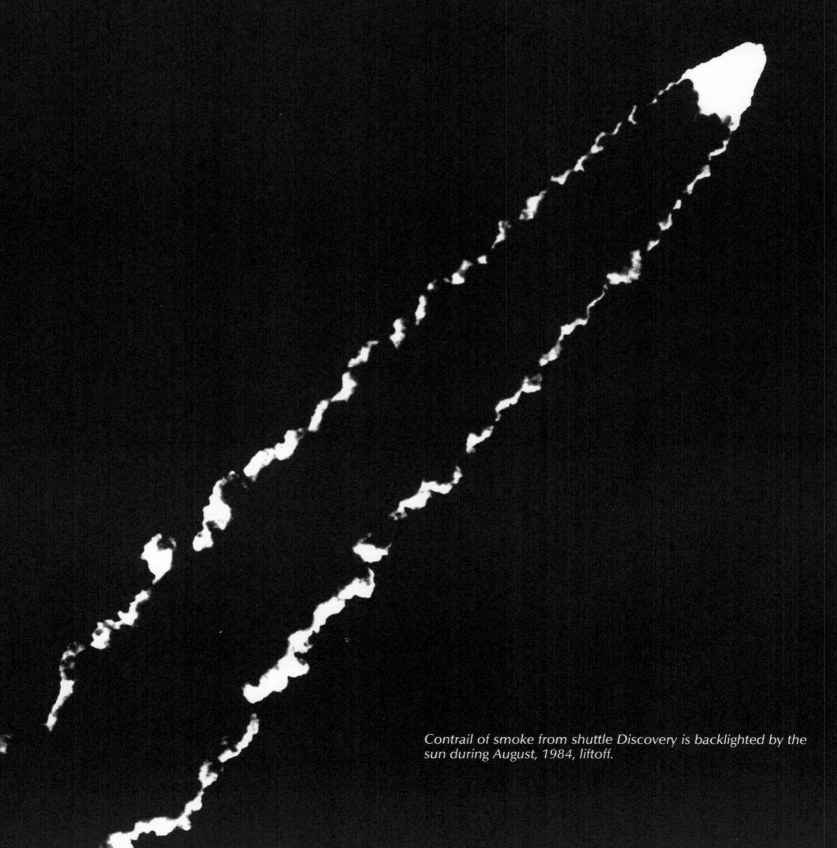

The shuttle Discovery made its maiden flight in August, 1984, and its astronauts deployed three commercial communications satellites for paying customers. The crew included Judy Resnik, America's second woman in space.

Contrail of smoke from shuttle Discovery is backlighted by the sun during August, 1984, liftoff.

SPACE FRISBEE

How the LEASAT communications satellite (SYNCOM IV) will be launched from the space shuttle Discovery

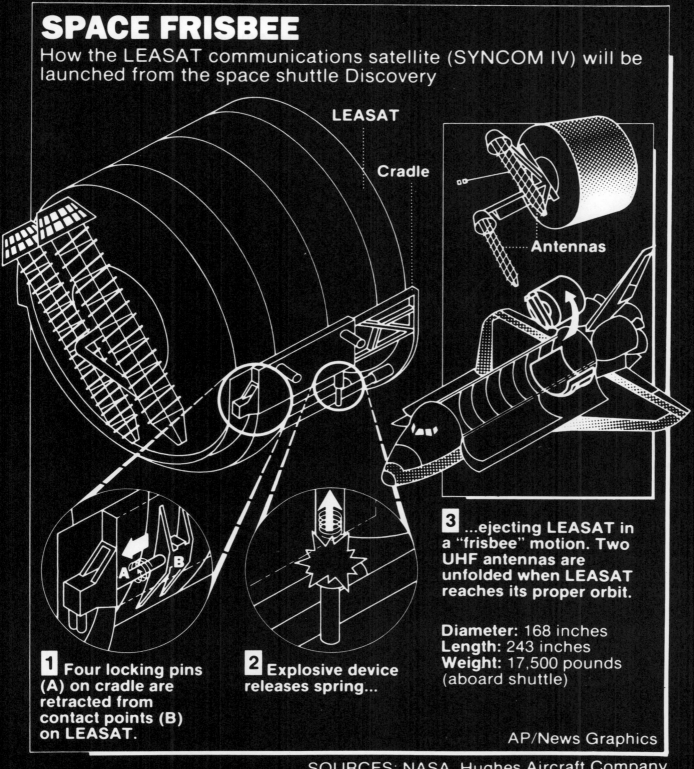

LEASAT

Cradle

Antennas

3 ...ejecting LEASAT in a "frisbee" motion. Two UHF antennas are unfolded when LEASAT reaches its proper orbit.

Diameter: 168 inches
Length: 243 inches
Weight: 17,500 pounds
(aboard shuttle)

1 Four locking pins (A) on cradle are retracted from contact points (B) on LEASAT.

2 Explosive device releases spring...

AP/News Graphics

SOURCES: NASA, Hughes Aircraft Company

Astronaut Judy Resnik on the shuttle Discovery, her hair standing out in zero gravity.

Crew of shuttle Discovery: (counter-clockwise from center) Henry Hartsfield Jr., Michael Coats, Steven Hawley, Judith Resnik, Charles Walker, and Richard Mullane.

Syncom satellite goes for orbit after release from shuttle Discovery.

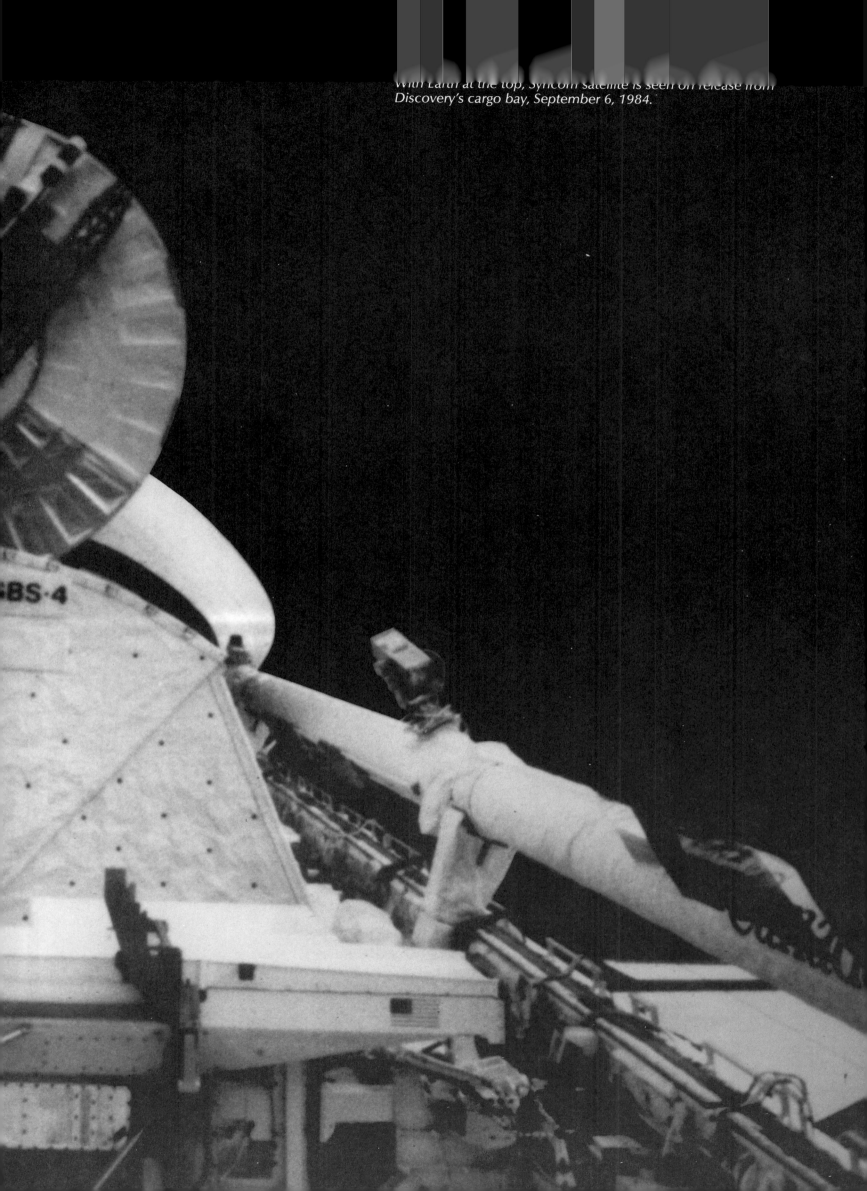

With Earth at the top, Syncom satellite is seen on release from Discovery's cargo bay, September 6, 1984.

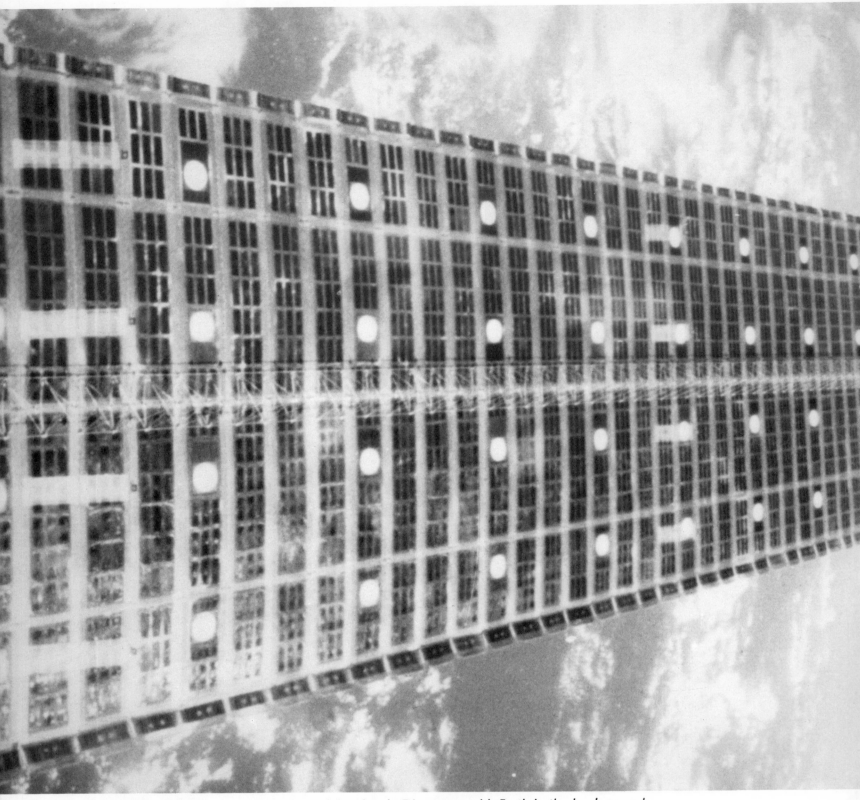

Solar Array panel extending from the cargo bay of the shuttle Discovery, with Earth in the background.

Artist's concept of testing of Solar Array flight experiment aboard Discovery.

Leaving for the launch pad at Kennedy Space Center for Challenger flight are (front) Kathy Sullivan (left) and Sally Ride; (behind, from left) Paul Scully-Power, Robert Crippen, Jon McBride, David Leestma, and Marc Garneau.

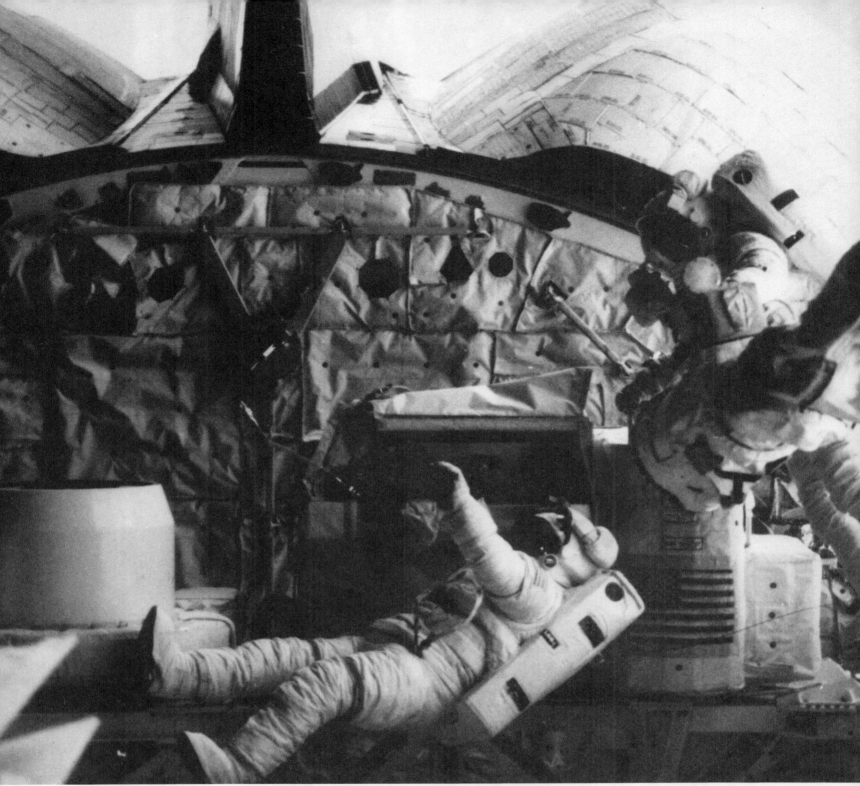

Astronauts David Leestma and Kathy Sullivan work at Challenger's orbital refueling system station.

Sally Ride was back in orbit on Challenger in October, 1984. She was part of a seven-person crew, the largest launched to that date. Among the members was another woman, Kathy Sullivan, who became the first American female to take a walk in space. She and David Leestma stepped through an airlock into the open cargo bay to practice techniques for refueling satellites in orbit.

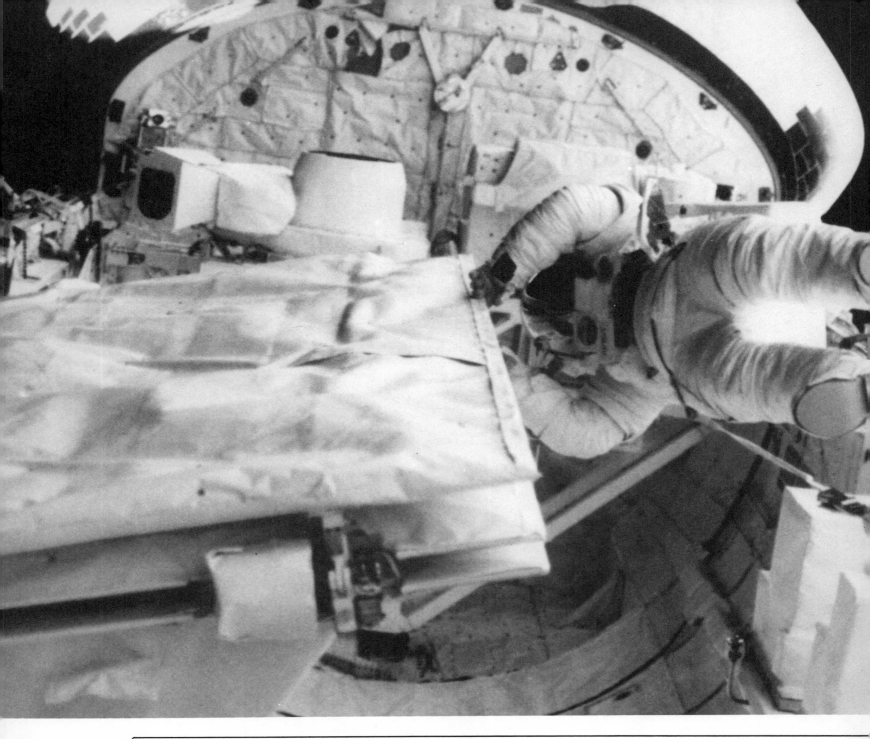

200

Kathy Sullivan, the first U.S. woman to walk in space, checking antenna closing during space walk in October, 1984.

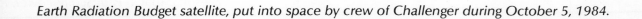
Earth Radiation Budget satellite, put into space by crew of Challenger during October 5, 1984.

Left: *Astronauts Kathy Sullivan (left) and Sally Ride show a "bag of space worms," a product of their creativity, aboard shuttle Challenger.*

Challenger crew, flight 10: (front) Jon McBride, Sally Ride, Kathy Sullivan, Dav
Leestma; (back) Paul Scully-Power, Robert Crippen, Marc Garne

Astronauts Kathy Sullivan and David Leestma perform in-space simulation of refueling another spacecraft in orbit.

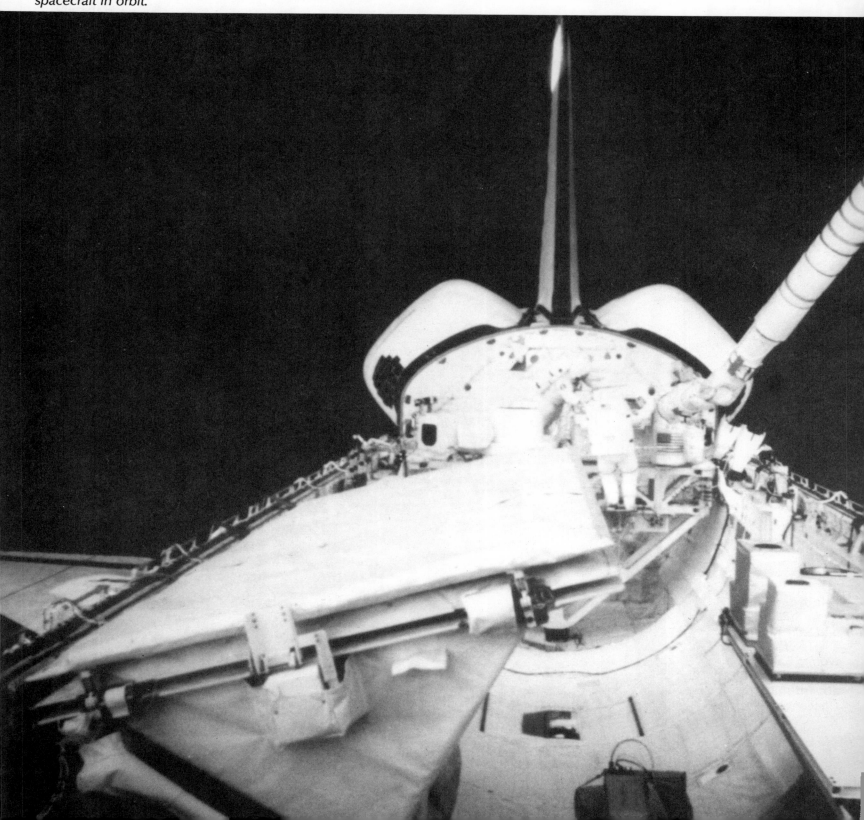

Astronaut Kathy Sullivan does some Earth viewing from shuttle Challenger during eight-day mission in 1984.

In a dramatic demonstration of the shuttle's capability, Discovery the next month tracked down in space two communications satellites that had fired into useless orbits after being successfully released by an earlier shuttle crew. Wearing the jet-pack, astronaut Joe Allen corraled the Palapa satellite, and he and Dale Gardner manhandled it into the cargo bay. Two days later it was Gardner's turn on the jet-pack, and he retrieved the Westar 6 satellite. both payloads were brought back to earth for repairs.

Discovery astronauts Joe Allen and Dale Gardner hold on to Westar satellite during recovery operations in 1984.

Anna Fisher, during shuttle Discovery flight in 1984.

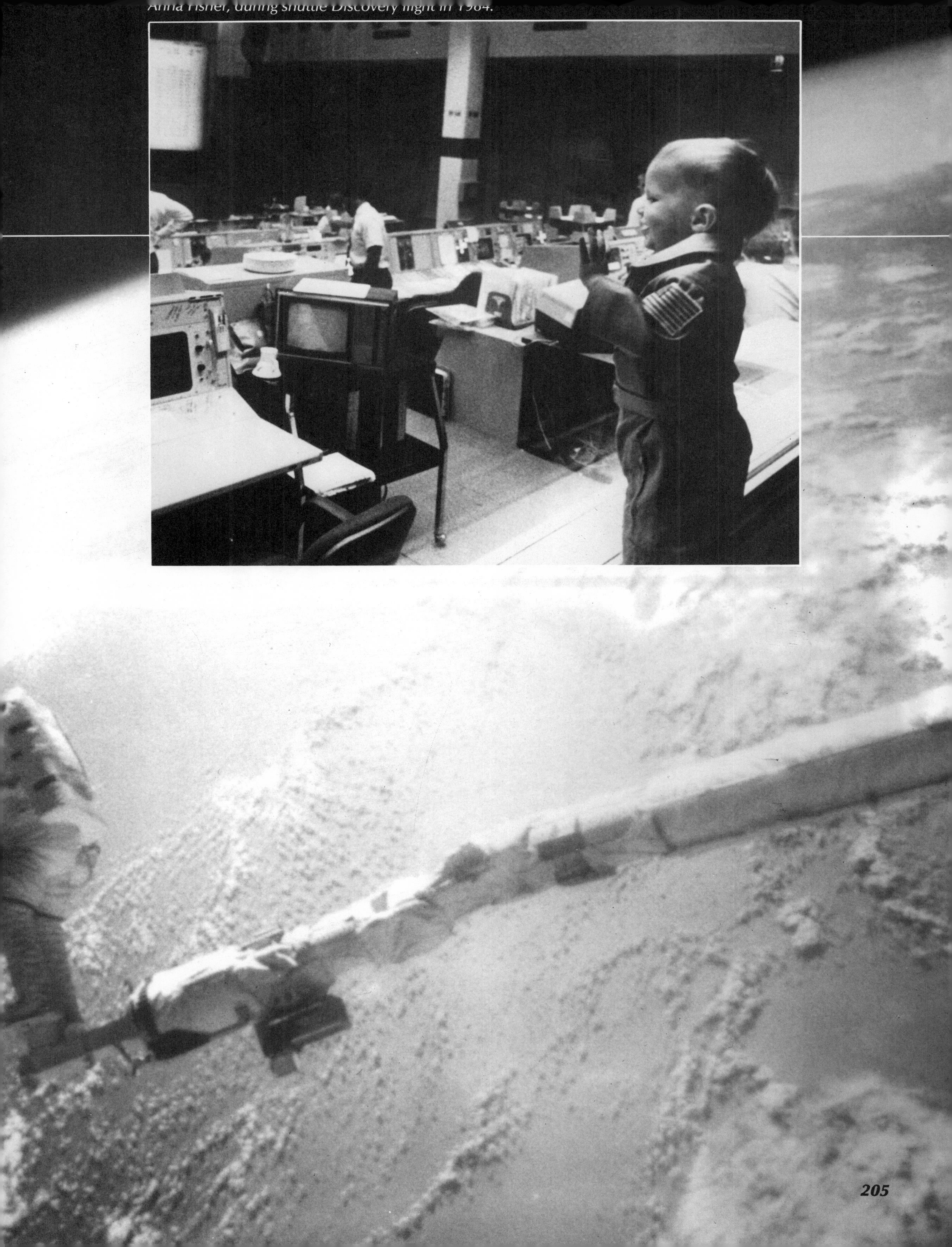

Astronaut Joe Allen with Westar satellite.

Shuttle Discovery crew after launching two communications satellites and recovering two wayward satellites: (left to right, front) David Walker, Anna Fisher, and Joe Allen; (back) Dale Gardner and Frederick Hauck.

Below: Astro-mom Anna Fisher kisses daughter Kristin after return from eight-day shuttle Discovery space mission.

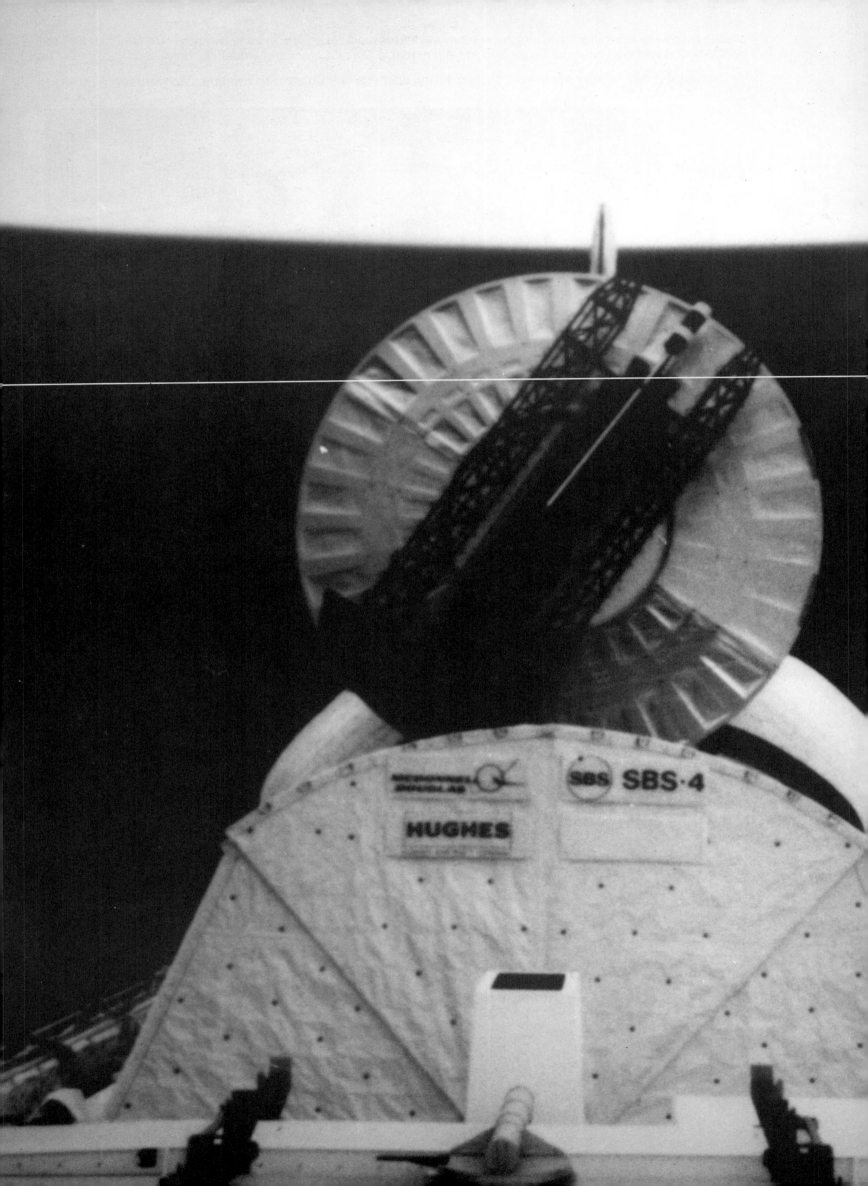

The shuttle got a new customer in January, 1985, when it carried up a secret spy satellite for the Defense Department. Because of the military nature of the mission, much of it was shrouded in secrecy.

The Pentagon has constructed its own shuttle launch facility at Vandenberg Air Force Base in California. By launching over water into north-south orbits from there, shuttle crews can fly over all areas of the globe. This can't be done from Cape Canaveral because a spaceship flying directly north or south from there would drop burned out booster rockets on populated areas.

Challenger pilot Roy Bridges and payload specialist Loren Acton on board the Challenger in July 1985.

Within a few years, shuttle crews flying out of Vandenberg will be testing laser and particle beams and other elements of President Reagan's plan to develop a defense against nuclear missiles. The president calls it his Strategic Defense Initiative. But most people know it as "Star Wars."

The shuttle also has been used on several flights as a laboratory in which the weightlessness and vacuum of space are used to produce materials that cannot be made on earth simply because certain things just do not mix in gravity. From this research could come purer crystals for electronic components, super-strong metal alloys and better medicines that might cure diabetes, certain types of cancer and other diseases.

An experimental package on the end of the robot arm of Challenger samples the environment over the cargo bay of the spaceship.

There were other new wrinkles in 1985. Senator Jake Garn, a Republican from Utah, became the first congressional observer on a shuttle mission. He requested the trip in his role as chairman of a subcommittee that oversees NASA's budget, and he saw firsthand the versatility of the man-machine combination. When a communications satellite launched by the astronauts failed to turn on its systems, astronauts Jeff Hoffman and David Griggs took an unplanned space walk to attach two makeshift "flyswatter"–shaped devices to the end of the robot arm. Commander Karol Bobko then guided Discovery to within a few feet of the satellite and Rhea Seddon reached out with the "flyswatters" and tugged on a switch, a move she hoped would turn on the satellite electrical power. But that was not the problem, and it didn't work. Nevertheless, Garn came home praising the astronauts for the effort.

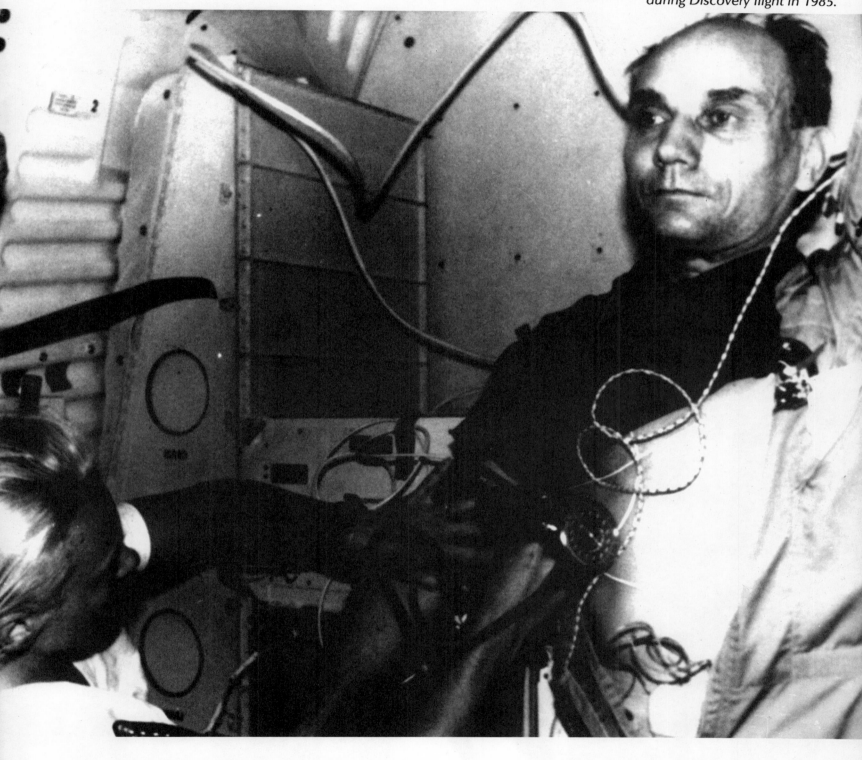

Mission specialist Rhea Siddon takes Senator Jake Garn's blood pressure during Discovery flight in 1985.

Space walker James van Hoften sends Syncom satellite back into space after repairs.

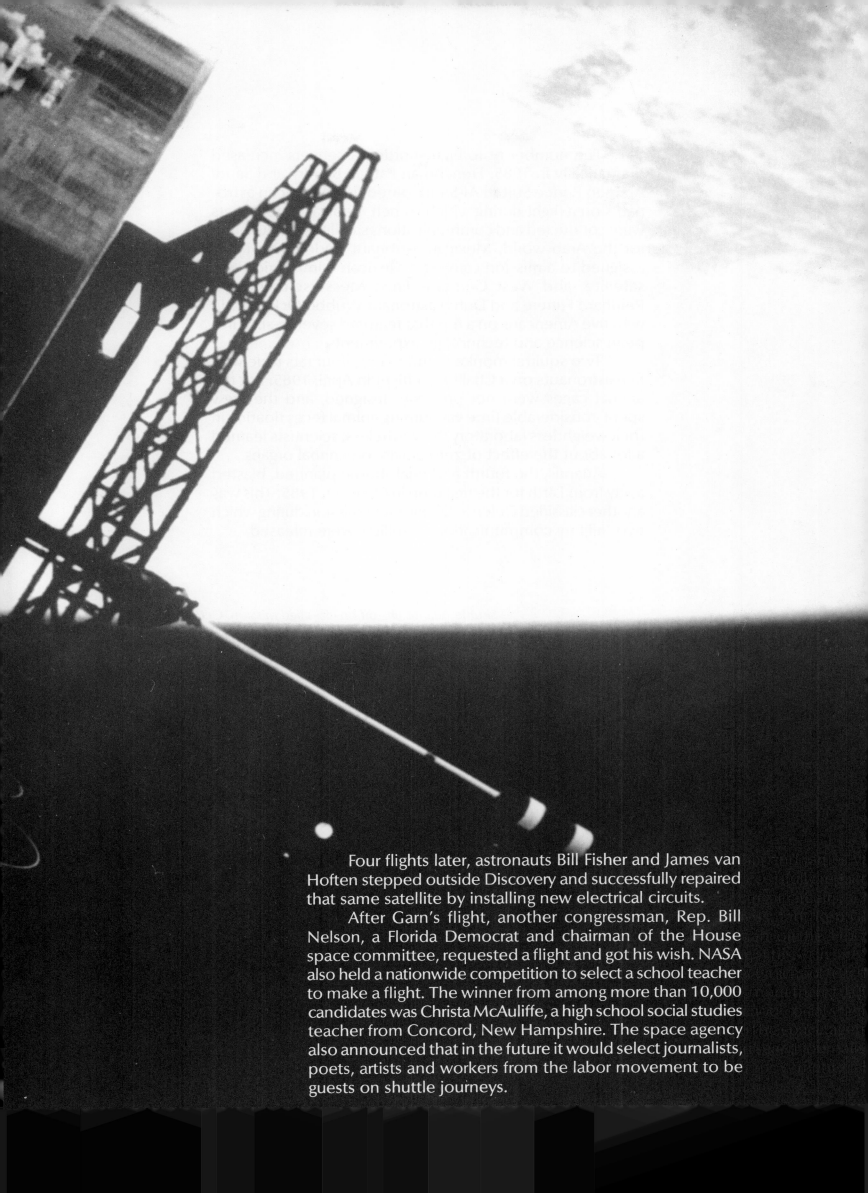

Four flights later, astronauts Bill Fisher and James van Hoften stepped outside Discovery and successfully repaired that same satellite by installing new electrical circuits.

After Garn's flight, another congressman, Rep. Bill Nelson, a Florida Democrat and chairman of the House space committee, requested a flight and got his wish. NASA also held a nationwide competition to select a school teacher to make a flight. The winner from among more than 10,000 candidates was Christa McAuliffe, a high school social studies teacher from Concord, New Hampshire. The space agency also announced that in the future it would select journalists, poets, artists and workers from the labor movement to be guests on shuttle journeys.

The number of foreign shuttle passengers increased dramatically in 1985. Frenchman Patrick Baudry and Saudi Arabian Prince Sultan Al-Saud joined five American astronauts on a flight during which French medical experiments were conducted and communications satellite was launched for the Arab world. Mexican astronaut Rudolfo Neri was assigned to a mission carrying a Mexican communications satellite, and West Germans Ernst Messerschmidt and Reinhard Furrere and Dutch astronaut Wubbo Ockels rode with five Americans on a trip that featured seventy-six European science and technology experiments.

Two squirrel monkeys and twenty-four rats rode with five astronauts on a Challenger flight in April, 1985. But the animal cages were not properly designed, and the crew spent considerable time vacuuming animal feces floating in their weightless laboratory. Nevertheless, scientists learned a lot about the effect of zero gravity on animal organs.

Atlantis, the fourth and final shuttle planned, blasted away from Earth for the first time in October, 1985. This was another classified Defense Department mission during which two military communications satellites were released.

Shuttle Atlantis lifts off on classified mission, October 3, 1985.

Sultan Salman Al-Saud (left) holds food tray on his lap as Patrick Baudry goes upside down while hooked up for medical experiments during Discovery flight in 1985.

Challenger crew on way to launch: (left to right) Ellison Onizuka, Gregory Jarvis, Christa McAuliffe, Mike Smith.

NASA photo via TV shows icicles hanging from Challenger pad structure early on the morning of Challenger's launch.

108

On January 28, 1986, the shuttle Challenger rocketed away from an icicle-laden launch pad at Cape Canaveral, overcoming finicky weather and faulty equipment to carry aloft a New Hampshire schoolteacher as NASA's first citizen in space.

Then, a little over a minute after launch, at 11:39:13 a.m. it happened; it happened before the stunned eyes of thousands watching at the Cape and millions more seeing it on television screens.

A catastrophic explosion blew apart the Challenger seventy-three seconds after liftoff, sending schoolteacher Christa McAuliffe and six NASA astronauts to a fiery death in the sky eight miles out from Kennedy Space Center.

Never before in fifty-six manned space flights had Americans died.

A slow-motion replay seemed to show an initial explosion occurred in one of the ship's two peel-away rocket boosters before the ship's huge external fuel tank burst into a fireball high above the Atlantic.

The explosion followed an apparently flawless launch, delayed for two hours as officials analyzed the danger from icicles that formed in the frosty Florida morning along the shuttle's new launch pad.

Schoolchildren watch Challenger lift off from Kennedy Space Center, cheering on the first schoolteacher-astronaut. The seven astronauts were killed just moments later.

Space shuttle Challenger lifts off on January 28, 1986. Moments later, it disintegrated.

There were apparently no signs of abnormalities on the screens as flight controllers monitored Challenger's liftoff and ascent. The blast seemed to occur unexpectedly and with absolutely no warning.

Mission Control reported that there had been no indication of any problem with the three shuttle engines, its twin solid boosters or any other system and that the shuttle just suddenly blew apart.

The explosion occurred as Challenger was 10.35 miles high and 8.05 miles downrange from the Cape, speeding toward orbit at 1,977 mph.

The crew included McAuliffe and six NASA astronauts: commander Francis R. Scobee, 46, pilot Michael J. Smith, 40; Judith Resnik, 36; Ronald F. McNair, 35; Ellison S. Onizuka, 39; and Gregory B. Jarvis, 41.

Words from space shuttle Challenger were all routine at the beginning of the flight. There was silence after the spacecraft erupted into a fireball.

Here is a transcript of those seconds:

MISSION COMMENTATOR: Ten-nine-eight-seven-six, we have main engine start, four-three-two-one, and liftoff. Liftoff of the twenty-fifth space shuttle mission. And it has cleared the tower.
SHUTTLE COMMANDER FRANCIS R. SCOBEE: Roll program.
MISSION CONTROL: Roger, roll, Challenger.
MISSION CONTROL COMMENTATOR: Roll program confirmed. Challenger now heading downrange. The engines are throttling down now at ninety-four percent. Normal throttle for most of the flight is one hundred four percent. We'll throttle down to sixty-five percent shortly. Engines at sixty-five percent. Three engines running normally. Three good fuel cells. Three good APUs (auxillary power units). Velocity 22,057 feet per

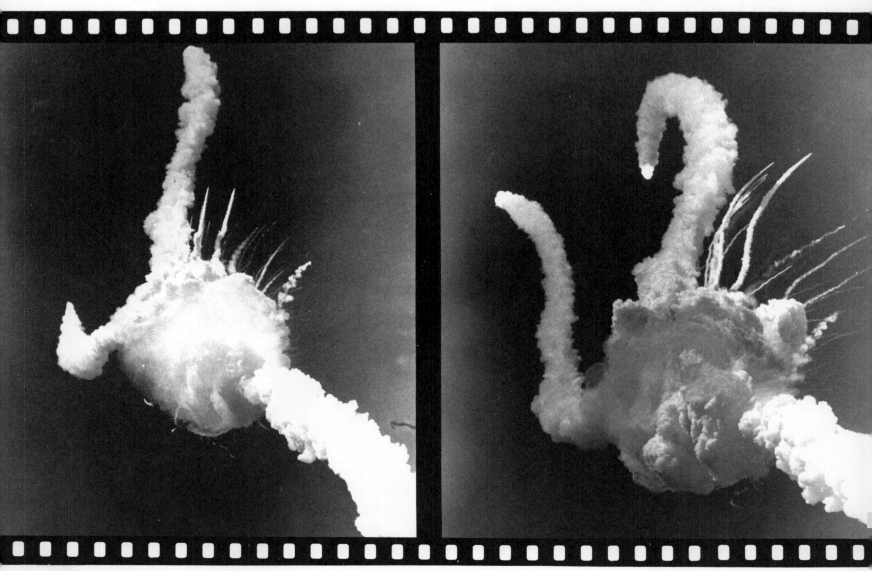

second (1,400 miles per hour), altitude 4.3 nautical miles (4.9 statute miles) downrange distance three nautical miles (3.4 statute miles). Engines throttling up, three engines now one hundred four percent.
MISSION CONTROL: Challenger, go at throttle up.
SCOBEE: Roger, go at throttle up.

(Fireball occurs)

MISSION CONTROL COMMENTATOR: We're at a minute fifteen seconds, velocity 2,900 feet per second (1,977 mph) altitude nine nautical miles (10.35 statute miles), range distance seven nautical miles (8.05 statute miles)

There was a long silence.

MISSION CONTROL COMMENTATOR: Flight controllers are looking very carefully at the situation. Obviously a major malfunction. We have no downlink (communications).

Lisa Corrigan, sister of Christa McAuliffe, reacts as she sees the shuttle Challenger explode. Behind her are parents Grace and Ed Corrigan.

Sequence shows shuttle Challenger blowing up shortly after liftoff.

From top to bottom:
Ellison S. Onizuka
Christa McAuliffe
Francis R. Scobee
Judith Resnik

President Reagan watched video replays in "stunned silence," and postponed the State of the Union message he was to deliver that night.

"It's a terrible thing," Reagan told reporters. "I just can't get out of my mind her (Mrs. McAuliffe) husband, her children as well as the families of the others on board."

"Oh, my God, no!" exclaimed first lady Nancy Reagan, who was watching the launch in the White House family quarters.

New Hampshire schoolchildren, drawn to this launch because of the presence of McAuliffe, the first "common citizen" chosen to make a space flight, screamed and fought back tears. Americans everywhere watched in disbelief as television networks replayed the shuttle explosion.

Lost along with the $1.2 billion spacecraft were a $100 million satellite that was to have become an important part of NASA's space-based shuttle communications network and a smaller $10 million payload that was to have studied Halley's comet.

It was the second disaster to strike NASA's pioneering space program. In 1967 — exactly nineteen years and one day before — astronauts Virgil "Gus" Grissom, Edward White and Roger Chaffee burned to death while preparing for an Apollo flight when a fire destroyed their capsule during a training drill.

Four Soviet cosmonauts died in space accidents — one in 1967 and three in 1971.

From top to bottom:
Gregory B. Jarvis
Ronald F. McNair
Michael J. Smith

In his televised tribute to the Americans killed on the space flight, President Reagan said:

"We will never forget them nor the last time we saw them, this morning as they prepared for their journey and waved goodbye and slipped the surly bonds of earth to touch the face of God."

This was a paraphrase of a poem, *High Flight*, written by John Gillespie Magee Jr., then nineteen, who was killed while serving as a volunteer with the Royal Canadian Air Force in World War II:

Oh, I have slipped the surly bonds of earth,
And danced the skies on laughter–silvered wings;
Sunward I've climbed and joined the tumbling mirth
Of sun-split clouds — and done a hundred things
You have not dreamed of — wheeled and soared and swung
High in the sunlit silence. Hov'ring there,
I've chased the shouting wind along and flung
My eager craft through footless halls of air.
Up, up the long, delirious, burning blue
I've topped the wind-swept heights with easy grace.
Where never lark, or even eagle, flew;
And, while with silent, lifting mind I've trod
The high, untrespassed sanctity of space,
Put out my hand, and touched the face of God.

Starting in the early 1990s, the shuttle fleet will be used to ferry into orbit the sections of a permanent manned space station. The sections will be assembled by astronaut construction workers.

Space station construction techniques were practiced in November 1985 by space-walkers Jerry Ross and Sherwood Spring, who stepped outside Atlantis and assembled girders and other structures, one extending forty-five feet above the shuttle's cargo bay.

President Reagan committed the United States to build the space station in his State of the Union message on January 25, 1984. The president said:

"America has always been greatest when we dared to be great. We can reach for greatness again. We can follow our dreams to distant stars, living and working in space for peaceful, economic and scientific gain. Tonight, I am directing NASA to develop a permanently-manned space station, and to do it within a decade.

"A space station will permit quantum leaps in our research in science, communications and in metals and life-saving medicines which can be manufactured only in space."

The space agency said an initial station, which would house six-to-eight persons, could be in orbit 300 miles high by 1992. The cost: $8 billion.

Artist's concept of a U.S. manned space station.

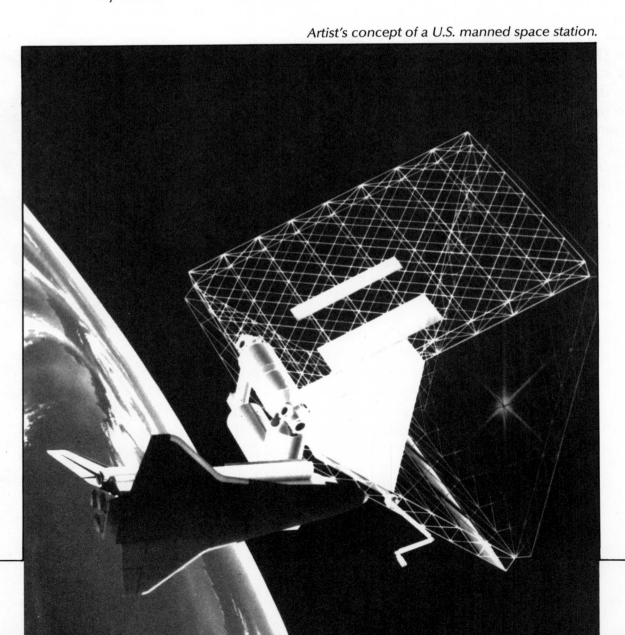

222

The station will be a center for a vast number of projects and for factories to produce medicines and materials. Satellites will be serviced and repaired there. And the city in the sky could enhance national security by providing a base for intelligence gathering and defense systems.

And, most important, the station would be a vital foothold in space — a staging area for fueling and launching spacecraft that will explore the solar system and help mankind establish a presence on the moon and beyond.

Most likely configuration is a central core to which astronauts will attach modules for living, manufacturing, power, fuel and for astronomy, medical and scientific experiments. As time passes, the basic station would be enlarged so that it could support one-hundred or more scientists, technicians and engineers. Perhaps even tourists one day.

NASA wants very much to construct a lunar base as its next goal after the station is operating. One of the strongest advocates is one of the first two men who walked on the moon — former astronaut Edwin "Buzz" Aldrin.

"The solar system's most desirable space station already has six American flags on it, and that's the moon," Aldrin said.

The moon could serve as an excellent scientific observation post, he said, and workers there could gradually construct a large solar power station to beam an enormous amount of electricity to earth.

The Apollo astronauts found there are unlimited supplies of certain materials on the moon that could be used to construct the moon base. This material also could be used to manufacture components of a space station or a probe to the planets. Because lunar gravity is just one-sixth of that on earth, these materials could be transported to the space station at just a fraction of the energy and cost needed to lift the same payload off the earth.

Sometime in the 21st century, the moon base could be the jumping off place for man's first journey to another planet. Mars appears to be the most hospitable, and it likely will be the first target. It will be a long voyage — seven months out, time for exploring the surface, and seven months back.

Beyond that, let your imagination run wild. And, maybe, in some future generation, astronaut John Young's prediction will come true. When he returned to earth after piloting Columbia on the first space shuttle mission, he said,

"The human race isn't far from going to the stars."